FIGHTING VEHICLES

FIGHTING VEHICLES

**Chris Ellis
Peter Chamberlain**

Hamlyn
London New York Sydney Toronto

FOREWORD

This book sets out to tell the story of the development of the armoured fighting vehicle in the age of mechanised warfare, a period roughly corresponding to the years from 1900 to the present. There have been many thousands of different armoured fighting vehicle (AFV) designs and we have mentioned and illustrated the most significant of them in this book.

Many famous campaigns and battles have involved the tactical use of armoured vehicles to greater or lesser degrees; in this book there is not space to dwell on them in detail but most are, nonetheless, mentioned in passing. Similarly, rather than pepper the text with technical facts and figures, we have provided a table at the back which gives some detailed comparative data for the most important AFV designs.

For assistance with the provision of photographs and other illustrations we wish to thank the following individuals and organisations: A. J. North; Hugh Howton; Colonel R. J. Icks, USAR (Retd); Major J. W. Loop, U.S. Army; Richard P. Hunnicutt, Alvis Limited; British Leyland; Noel Ayliffe-Jones; D. Mayne; G. Pavey; the Photographic Library, Imperial War Museum, London; and the Central Office of Information. The small drawings are by Kenneth M. Jones.

CE/PC

Published by The Hamlyn Publishing Group Limited
London · New York · Sydney · Toronto
Hamlyn House, Feltham, Middlesex, England
Copyright © The Hamlyn Publishing Group Limited 1972

Second Impression 1973

ISBN 0 600 33481 3

Printed in England by Sir Joseph Causton and Sons Limited

CONTENTS

THE COMING OF ARMOUR

The modern armoured vehicle is as much a product of the industrial age as the motor car or the aircraft, although the idea of armoured forces dates back of course to the beginning of history. The war elephant, the war chariot, and

During the Crimean War in 1855 one Englishman suggested taking one of the then new steam traction engines, putting an armour cover round the driver and fitting big scythes to the wheelhubs. The notion was dismissed

jects were either produced or projected but none was successful. Traction engines saw wide military use however, mainly for towing guns and wagons.

Armoured traction engines were used with success by the British during the Boer war; here supply columns were subject to attack by Boer commandos and to combat this the Fowler company armoured four vehicles with boiler plate. Each towed four special armoured wagons which could each hold either one field gun or 30 men. Loopholes were provided for rifle fire from within the trailer. Within their limitations these armoured Fowlers were remarkably successful.

The coming of the internal combustion engine and the passenger motor car gave the first major impetus to the development of mobile gun carriers. Several imaginative individuals saw the potential and produced designs or actual prototypes of what were then generally called 'war cars'. In Britain in 1898 a motor engineer, Frederick Simms, built and demonstrated a motorised quadricycle which carried a shielded Maxim machine gun at the front. In America the same year, Colonel R. P. Davidson, commander of a military academy, had a Duryea car converted on similar lines, with a front-mounted Colt machine gun. This started life as a three-wheeler, but was later converted to a four-wheeler like Simms' machine. In 1900 Davidson had two steam cars built mounting Colt machine guns, and all these vehicles were used on academy training exercises. They formed the first ever organised mechanised patrol force, though they were virtually 'private', not part of the official US Army.

The armoured Fowler B5 traction engine of 1900 was one of the first practical armoured vehicles. Four were used to protect supply columns in the Boer War; the armoured trailers carried infantry.

the phalanx were the tactical units of armoured force in their day. With the coming of mechanical power and workable iron and steel plate in the 19th century, military men in various parts of the world saw how the new technology could be harnessed to military requirements. Cugnot produced a rudimentary – and largely unsuccessful – steam carriage in 1769 and postulated a military use for it as an artillery tractor.

as 'barbaric' by the government. In that year, however, the British Army bought its first Boydell traction engines which were used to tow guns at Woolwich Arsenal. These vehicles had 'footed' wheels, a rudimentary form of endless tracks round the wheels.

In America during the Civil War, a steam tractor was given an armoured cover and fitted with a muzzle-loader gun at one end which could fire balls of various sizes. Built by one Ross Winans in 1861, the vehicle was taken to Harpers Ferry by the Confederates, where it was promptly captured. It was not used again.

Various other traction engine pro-

The first true armoured car designs appeared in 1900. In Russia an armoured steam car called the Divinski was built for the artillery, but it was grossly underpowered and was never used. In Britain the American engineer E. J. Pennington put an armoured skirt round the body of a 16 hp car and fitted it with shielded Maxim guns front and rear. The military authorities were not interested, however, and no further progress was made with this.

In France a cavalry officer, motoring enthusiast and race driver called Genty persuaded his general to acquire a Panhard car which was modified by the manufacturers to feature armament. A shielded Hotchkiss machine gun was fitted and the car was successfully used for patrol work in Morocco in 1902.

Back in Britain in 1902, Simms unveiled a new design, his 'war car' which was a very large $6\frac{1}{4}$ ton vehicle, 28 ft long. It consisted of a heavy car chassis to which a faired armour skirt was attached by elliptic springs. A pompom quick-firer gun and two machine guns were carried, later altered by the addition of closed armoured barbettes. The driver controlled the deep-sided vehicle standing at a central column. Though the 'War Car' got extensive publicity through demonstrations it again failed to rouse the interest of the War Office.

Two Charron partly armoured cars

Left: this Hotchkiss 'automitrailleuse' built in 1909 was a tourer with a machine gun in a tub-like turret at the rear. Four were supplied to the Sultan of Turkey. The 1904 Charron (below left) was a true armoured car, with an enclosed steel body, armoured bonnet and turret and sand channels.
Right: between 1907 and 1909 the British Army experimented with crawler tractors for artillery haulage, among them this prototype Ruston Hornsby. De Mole's original drawings for a crawler track military vehicle anticipate subsequent tank designs to a remarkable degree; submitted to the War Office in 1912, this was not taken up.
Below: a four-wheel drive Austro-Daimler 'panzerwagen' of 1904. It had light (3 mm) armour, a Maxim gun as armament, and a top speed of 28 mph.

were built in France in 1904, based on saloon car bodies. A hand-traversing machine gun turret was fitted on the roof over the rear seats. One was purchased by the Russians and the other was used by the French in Morocco. In 1904 the German army tried an Austro-Daimler car with an enclosed dome-like turret.

These were essentially modified passenger cars but in 1908 Armstrong-Whitworth brought out a 40 hp design built specially as an armoured car. This had a winch for hauling itself out of mud, and the hull was laid out to give a good forward mounting for the gun alongside the driver. The designer was W. G. Wilson, who a few years later played a major part in designing the first British tank. Russia later bought one of these Armstrong-Whitworths, differing from the original in having the gun in a turret (the Russians also used several French and German armoured cars, having discovered quite early that such vehicles were useful for border patrols).

The Italians were the first to actually use armoured cars in combat, in 1912 during the Italian-Turkish wars in North Africa. The Italian Army's car was an Isotta-Fraschini which had a box-like body with hand-traversed turret and machine gun. It was simple and reliable, based on a 35 hp chassis used for limousines.

In the early years of the 20th Century the idea of tanks, or 'landships' was

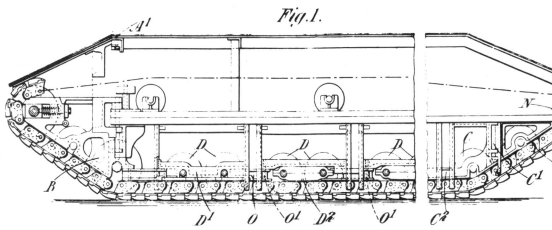

Fig.1.

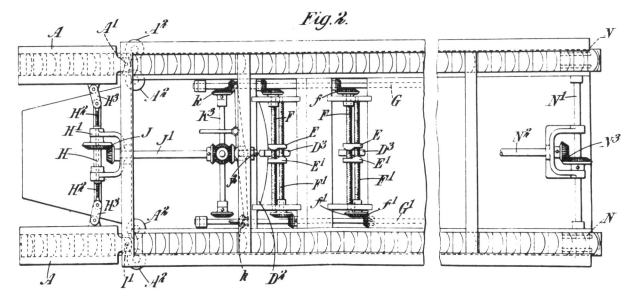

Fig.2.

sented a design for a crawler track vehicle to the British War Office. He had originally designed the vehicle for store carrying over rough country in the outback. He saw the military potential and, with modifications, sent his design to Britain. The War Office rejected it, however, having no interest in crawler track vehicles at that time. De Mole's design was rhomboid in shape, similar to the tanks which were actually built some years later. Steering was accomplished by turning the front and rear bogies, and the tracks were sprung.

Freidrich Goble in Germany was the last of this band of tank pioneers who were active before their time. He produced a 'Panzerlandkreuzer' (armoured land cruiser) in 1913 which had 'walking' legs not unlike the style of weighted legs on a child's walking toy (there was no directional control however). It had a torpedo shaped body and Goble built a working model to demonstrate to the German War Office. Goble was asked to build a full-size vehicle to some strict basic requirements, including 50 ft turning radius and speed of $7\frac{1}{2}$ mph. Nothing more was heard of this, but in 1915 Goble came out with another design which had a form of continuous track; again it had no means of steering and was rejected. Goble's last attempt at tank design, also in 1915, involved a small scale model running on a rail type of track and elliptical balls, and again ended in failure.

In August 1914, Europe went to war, with the armoured car a proven and practical idea but not one which endeared itself to generals or military leaders. Events of the following few years were, however, to assure armoured vehicles of their place in history.

already in the minds of some military men. This was the age of popular science fiction when writers like Jules Verne and H. G. Wells had described futuristic crawling vehicles, bristling with guns. Quite clearly this was the starting point for several 'landship' ideas which were postulated well before the First World War.

A French artillery officer, Captain la Vavasseur, drew up a plan for a crawler track armoured vehicle in the 1903–1905 period. This had a square box-like structure with tracks each side and the gun pointing out at the front. The army had no interest in the idea, however, and the project lapsed.

In 1911, an Austrian officer Gunther Burstyn, was inspired by an early American Holt crawler track agricultural tractor to draw up a design for a vehicle based on this type of chassis, surmounted by an armoured super-structure with a central turret and machine gun. He sent the designs to the Austrian War Office, who said they would be pleased to see it if Burstyn could build a prototype at his own expense. Burstyn was discouraged, and sent the idea to the German War Office, who rejected it on the grounds that it infringed patents for agricultural tractors! So Burstyn's 'Motor Geschutze' (motor-gun) was dropped; it was, however, undoubtedly a practical proposition and had most of the features later found in tank designs.

An Australian, L. de Mole, next pre-

ARMOUR IN THE FIRST WORLD WAR

Despite the promising development of armoured cars in the years before 1914 and the dashing tactics which went with them, the armies which marched to war in August 1914 were still best suited to the musket and cavalry age, in training and equipment, if not in spirit. True the rifle gave the infantry-man good stopping power, and the machine gun was part of infantry battalion equipment, but little else had changed since the 19th century.

The French Army in 1914 still wore their traditional blue and red and their cavalry went to war in breastplates and crested helmets. In all armies, cavalry was still considered the most important arm, the favourite of the generals, and there was still a majority of senior officers who declared the machine gun 'unsporting'.

The British Army was particularly meagrely equipped with machine guns in 1914, the scale being only two per battalion. The horse was the all-important means of transport at this time and mechanical vehicles were in only limited service.

During the first four weeks of fighting on the Western Front, there was plenty of movement as the vast well-equipped German Army raced through Belgium in a right-hook march on Paris, the classic Schlieffen Plan. Britain's small expeditionary force made a gallant but unsuccessful stand at Mons, but the Germans were not finally checked until they reached the Marne. An early and effective demonstration of the value of motor transport was made here when Marshal Foch commandeered every taxi in Paris in his urgent quest to move reinforcements quickly to the Front. The British Marines at about the same time

hastily pressed London omnibuses into service at Antwerp, again as troop carriers. Subsequently several hundred of these vehicles (complete with crews) were taken from the London streets, 'enlisted' for the duration of the war with windows boarded up and peace-time liveries overpainted khaki or grey. These extemporisations had nothing to do with armoured vehicle development, but they set a pattern for future mechanisation which came about on a grand scale as the war progressed.

From the Marne the Germans retreated to the Aisne, and it was here that the war of movement ceased, virtually for the duration. For now the Germans demonstrated the supremacy of the machine gun and the gun barrage as a 'man stopper'. A few well placed machine guns could dominate a battlefield and decimate infantry advances. The infantry dug trenches to make a protected line and a gun barrage then attempted to pulverise the trenches. And of these vital weapons the Germans had a preponderance in the early days of the war.

Thus the familiar pattern of fighting which has become synonymous with the image of the First World War was set – long and extensive lines of trenches, elaborate barbed wire defences, a mass of mud turned up by incessant shell fire and short, sometimes futile, infantry attacks when any advances recorded were measured more often in yards than in miles.

These were the circumstances which led directly to the development of the machine which was to become a major weapon of war – the tank.

The first armoured vehicles to see action, however, were armoured cars, which were used from the earliest days

of the war (although not as part of the military effort in the British case). Paradoxically enough it was the Royal Navy, specifically the Royal Naval Air Service, which showed the potential of the armoured vehicle and initiated the ideas which led up to tank development. The RNAS was charged with the defence of Antwerp and other North Sea ports in August and September 1914, with land planes and sea-planes which flew reconnaisance and harassment sorties against the enemy. To protect the landing grounds in an economic manner – there were no spare men to march about with rifles – the RNAS commander suggested to the First Lord of the Admiralty, Winston Churchill, that 50 motor cars should be acquired, fitted with guns and used for patrol work. These could also rush to the rescue of pilots of aircraft which crashed near enemy troops. Churchill agreed, but doubled the number to 100 and specified the best available car – the Rolls-Royce (in fact, Talbots and Wolseleys were also used since the Rolls was in short supply).

On arrival in Belgium the first cars were crudely armoured with locally obtained steel plates. These proved successful, though the plates were not bullet proof, so arrangements were made to armour subsequent cars in Britain before they were sent to the front. These vehicles – the Admiralty Pattern armoured cars – had reinforced springs, dual rear wheels and quite elaborate armoured bodies. A further development was the classic Rolls-Royce Admiralty Turreted Pattern armoured car with a fully enclosed body and hand-worked centre turret, the scheme being worked out by the

Above: the classic Rolls-Royce Admiralty Pattern armoured car in service in 1916.
Left: the Seabrook armoured truck, showing drop sides and its 3 pdr quick firer gun.
Right, top: Belgian troops with an armoured car improvised on a Minerva touring car in 1914.
Right: Austin armoured cars on the Western Front in August 1918. The twin turrets are a distinctive feature.

RNAS armoured car commanders based on operating experience. This design was widely used for the rest of the war, served on all fronts, and remained in service (in a few cases) well into the 1930s, even though later Rolls-Royce armoured car designs had appeared. Lanchesters, Talbots, and Delaunay-Bellevilles were also produced to this same basic turreted design to supplement the Rolls.

To supplement and support their armoured car force, the RNAS were supplied with some new heavy vehicles built on the American 5 ton Seabrook lorry chassis. The bodies were constructed in Britain and had drop sides, armoured bonnets and cabs. A 3 pdr naval gun and four Maxim machine guns were mounted in the back. These vehicles came into service early in 1915. They were most formidable and effective so long as they kept to the roads. Elsewhere they suffered the penalties for having a body too heavy for the chassis – the overall weight was 10 tons – and they were not successful on soft ground. Later in 1915 they were taken out of service.

The Belgian forces emulated the RNAS and quickly armoured some Minerva touring cars, which made powerful and most effective fighting vehicles. The Germans in turn captured some of these and used them against their former owners, at the same time copying the idea in conversions of their own staff cars. Thus in one corner of Europe a detached and inter-

Opposite, top: the Tank Mk.IX – the 'Pig' – was a purpose-built supply and troop carrier, built too late to see service in the First World War. The Tank Mk.VIII, the 'Liberty' or 'International', was the ultimate Allied tank design. This is the British prototype; production, in 1919, was limited to an American batch of 100 vehicles.

The Tank Mk.IV (above) was the principal British type in 1917. It was directly developed from the original Mk.I and has the classic rhomboid shape. This is a 'Female', with machine gun armament.

The Daimler (top) and Erhardt (below), together with a Büssing, were armoured cars built to German War office requirements in 1915. The Erhardt – this a 1917 model – became the main production type.

mittent form of armoured warfare was going on long before armoured cars were used elsewhere and long before the tank finally appeared.

Numerically the most important of British armoured cars was the Austin. Initially this type was built to the order of the Russian Government, but after the Revolution of 1917 vehicles still in hand were given to the British Army. In the last year of the war they were widely used in Mesopotamia and Persia as well as on the Western Front. Twin turrets and pneumatic tyres, plus a rear steering position were refinements introduced. A standard 30 hp Austin tourer chassis was used and spare wheels were carried in the superstructure underneath the turret barbettes. Austins led the British troops into Berlin after the Armistice in 1918.

Rolls-Royces were used occasionally on the Western Front (later by the Army as well as the RNAS), in Egypt, East Africa, and in Palestine and Iraq with Colonel T. E. Lawrence's irregulars. Three vehicles were even landed at Gallipoli although there was to be no chance to use them in that abortive campaign.

Following the early 1914 experiences with armoured cars the Germans took them up in a small way. Typically the German War Office laid down fairly precise specifications. All designs were to have four wheel drive and emergency rear steering positions as well as normal controls. All were to have machine guns in rotating turrets and extensive machine gun armament in the hull. These features, years later, were to become common to all armoured cars.

By late 1915 the war of movement on the Western Front had ceased and the need for armoured cars had gone. However, the German vehicles were formed into a unit and sent on operations near Verdun early in 1916. Opportunities for their employment were non-existent and later in the year the cars were transferred to the Transylvania front to fight against the Rumanians.

The Germans were also the first to build an armoured troop carrying truck, the Mannesman-Mulag which appeared in 1916, some years before this type of vehicle became common; it does not appear to have been used in combat.

Meanwhile the designs for the first tanks, or 'landships' as they were then called were being worked out in 1915. Both Britain and France actually worked on ideas each unknown to the other. However, the first practical tank was built in Britain and the British were the first to have tanks in service and in action. The ever-resourceful Royal Naval Air Service made all the early progress, under the direction of Captain Sueter.

Fighting over ground churned to mud by constant shell fire and raked by machine guns emphasised the infantry's need for some sort of armour protection – a shield on wheels seemed the obvious answer. Such a device was first mocked-up by the RNAS in England but it proved too heavy for its wheels, and would in any case have been difficult to push over muddy ground. As an alternative to wheels, Sueter was inspired to use rubber 'endless' tracks such as were made by the London firm of Diplock under the trade name of Pedrail, and Pedrail tracks were adapted to the original infantry shield idea (subsequently abandoned as impracticable).

Sueter then suggested a 'landship', utilising the largest possible Pedrail tracks each driven by an engine, the whole machine to be articulated for ease of movement across country. An enveloping armoured body with a 12 pdr naval gun in front was to provide cover for an 8 man crew.

Another RNAS officer, Commander Hetherington, suggested a 'big wheel' machine for attacking enemy trenches – a tricycle arrangement of 45 ft wheels carrying an armoured body with three twin 4 inch naval gun mounts. Hetherington worked out mathematically that these large wheels would easily ride over any trench or breastwork. To examine the feasibility of these rival ideas, Churchill set up a 'Landships Committee' on February 20, 1915, to commend or suggest the best idea. This was headed by the Chief of Naval Construction.

Limited progress was made with the Pedrail machine. Its function was changed from a gun carrier to an infantry carrier specifically for trench raiding parties rather than as an assault vehicle in its own right. A major problem was in the articulation of the two halves and the only Pedrail vehicle built later reverted to a single frame chassis for simplicity. The Pedrail tracks were driven by belts from the drive shafts of two transversely mounted Rolls-Royce engines. By the time this vehicle was completed in 1917 the tank had been perfected and it thus passed from the scene of tank development.

The early obsession for capturing the enemy trenches led to a number of further ideas. Churchill himself had the somewhat impractical notion of using two steam rollers lashed together side by side. A very ingenious idea was the Tritton trench crossing machine, another project sponsored by Churchill and tested (with no great success) in May 1915. This was a standard Daimler–Foster petrol-electric tractor (used by the Royal Marines to haul guns) with an extended nose which carried two 15 ft bridge spans on an endless chain. The vehicle was headed for a trench, pushed its nose to the far side, after which a front control wheel was used to lower the bridge sections to the parapet. The vehicle ran over them and dragged the girders clear behind it as it passed over the trench. Reversing the vehicle brought the girders back into position for another crossing. This idea was never taken up, though in retrospect it proved to be the as then unwanted forerunner of the mobile bridge layer, later to become an important specialist armoured vehicle.

While the RNAS evolved their ideas for 'landships' an army staff officer, Colonel E. D. Swinton, who was attached to British H.Q. in France as an official correspondent, had similar thoughts. He postulated an armoured infantry carrier which could be made by putting an armoured body on to an American Holt tractor. The Holt 75 hp tractor was one of the most significant vehicles in the history of mechanised warfare, for it later formed the basis for the first French, German and American tanks. It played no further part in British tank development, however, for Swinton's idea was not seriously followed up when put before the Committee of Imperial Defence in November 1914, even though it was enthusiastically endorsed by Churchill. Army interest in the matter ended for the time being in January 1915 after a perfunctory official test which led to the rejection of the Holt as unsuitable. The test failed mainly because the vehicle was overloaded and made to tow a trailer, which was not part of Swinton's idea.

Meanwhile the enterprising RNAS Landships Committee were seeking better tracks than the Pedrail offered. In America crawler track tractors had long been in production for agricultural use, and two RNAS officers were dispatched to America to examine and purchase suitable tractors on the Committee's behalf. One of these was the interesting Killen-Strait tractor, which had its tracks in tricycle formation, the front one being dumb (and given a direction indicator) and steered the vehicle. The two rear tracks were driven. The Killen-Strait tracks were not big enough for 'landship' use but nevertheless the vehicle was demonstrated to Churchill and the Munitions Minister Lloyd-George at the RNAS testing and development depot at

Wormwood Scrubs in June 1915. The tracks on this vehicle were of hardwood sheathed in steel. The trials, over a variety of obstacles, were most successful in proving the advantage of tracked vehicles. The following month the body (less turret) of a Delaunay-Belleville armoured car was added to the Killen-Strait chassis. This made it into Britain's first armoured tracked vehicle (although it was not intended, of course, for combat).

The other type of tractor purchased in America was the Bullock 'Creeping Grip' vehicle, another agricultural type with front wheels for steering and short track units at the rear. The idea here was to use two of these lengthy tractors articulated to form a chassis for Sueter's original RNAS 'Landship' proposal and so overcome the limitations of the Pedrail track version. Two Bullock vehicles were duly purchased and were tested in June 1915. However, the stress between the two vehicles on uneven ground proved that the idea of articulated vehicles was impractical in all but ideal ground conditions. Experiments were continued for a while, but the articulated idea was abandoned and in late July 1915 the Landship

Committee asked Sir William Tritton, of the famous engineering firm of Fosters of Lincoln (and a co-opted member of the committee), to design a 'landship' which would be virtually equal to one half of the old articulated vehicle design. Tritton worked with Major W. G. Wilson, a leading mechanical engineer, using lengthened Bullock tracks and the Daimler engine, gearbox and drive from the 105 hp Daimler–Foster tractor made by Tritton's firm. The resulting vehicle had a box-like body, steerable wheels on a 'tail' extension and provision for a rotating turret with a 2 pdr gun on top of the body in armoured car fashion. This turret was never fitted, however. Known as the 'No. 1 Lincoln Machine', it was nicknamed 'Little Willie', either after the popular sobriquet for the German Crown Prince or William Tritton.

This first practical tank design was tested early in September 1915. The Bullock tracks proved inadequate for

Tritton 'trench crossing machine', showing the bridge in place over a ditch; the control wheel and recovery chains can be clearly seen. Vehicle proved unwieldy and impractical

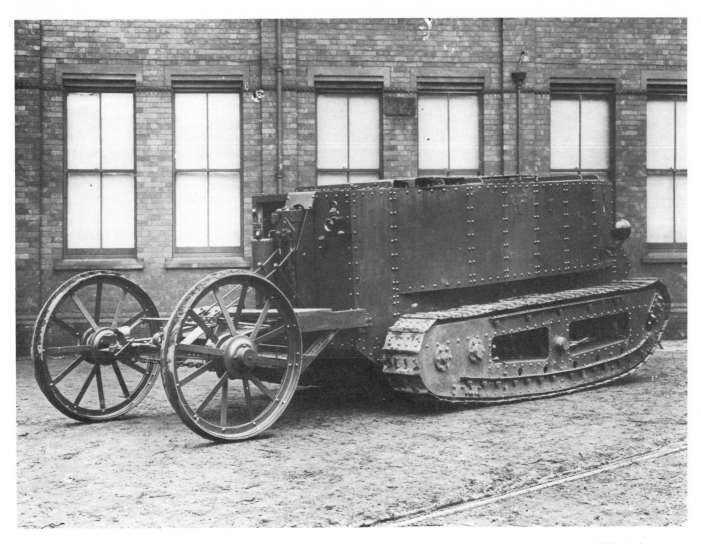

their task, however, lacking strength and flexibility, so Tritton and Wilson subsequently designed new tracks with pressed steel shoes running on guides in track frames. So modified, the vehicle emerged for new trials in December 1915 shrouded in tarpaulins to conceal its purpose to onlookers.

Even before 'Little Willie' had been completed Tritton and Wilson had begun to think of its successor. What was proved in 'Little Willie's' early trials was that the centre of gravity was too high in a vehicle with low tracks and a heavy superstructure. This limited the all important trench-crossing ability, a major requirement of the time, to $4\frac{1}{2}$–$5\frac{1}{2}$ ft, whereas the latest War Office specifications stipulated a trench crossing ability of 9 ft. Similarly the height of the vehicle above its tracks made it unstable beyond a very gentle angle of tilt. Clearly a fundamental change was desirable.

The answer was found early in 1915 by recourse to the 'Big Wheel' theory which had earlier been put forward by Commander Hetherington of the

RNAS as an alternative to the tracked 'Landship' idea. The Landships Committee had started to build a 'Big Wheel' mock-up with 15 ft diameter wheels, but even this could be seen to be impractical both for handling and because of its large size, which would have offered a generous target for enemy guns. Tritton and Wilson now hit on brilliant idea and returned to the 'Big Wheel' idea for their redesigned tracked vehicle. Their answer to the trench-crossing problem was to make the lower run of the track approximate as closely as possible to an arc from a theoretical 45 ft diameter wheel. In other words the section in ground contact formed the arc, but the flexible track obviated the need for a large circumference of tread. To overcome the problem of instability they took the tracks round the full height of the vehicle, thus arriving at the rhomboid or 'lozenge' which has traditionally characterised the classic shape ever since.

In the new design the idea of a turret was dropped in favour of guns in side

sponsons, which also to help lower the centre of gravity. The prototype was called 'Mother' or 'Big Willie'. The hull structure, though largely concealed by the track frames was actually similar to that of 'Little Willie'. The driver and commander sat at the front with gearsmen and brakesmen standing each side of the centrally mounted Daimler engine and working in response to hand signals from the driver. Drive was via half shafts which worked gears and chains to the sprockets in the rear horns. An interesting feature was the wheeled steering 'tail', a spring loaded trolley at the back of the vehicle intended partly to give extra stability and partly as a rudder which facilitated large radius turns and thus obviated the need to change gear or brake. Small radius turns were made by braking one or other of the tracks.

'Mother' was completed and dem-

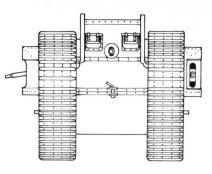

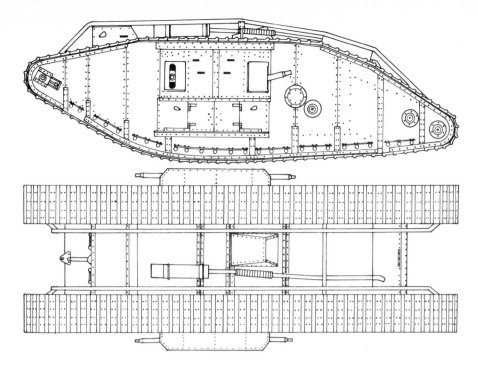

onstrated to high ranking government officials and War Office personnel in January 1916. The response was enthusiastic, though Lord Kitchener, Minister of War, regarded it somewhat contemptuously as a 'pretty mechanical toy'.

The success of 'Mother' led in February 1916 to a production order for 100 vehicles of the same type. It was at this time that the name 'tank' came into use as a generic term, mainly for security reasons, the name 'landship' being too descriptive. To enquirers and factory workers the new vehicles – built under conditions of top security – were described as 'water carriers' or 'water tanks', soon abbreviated to 'tanks'.

To operate the new vehicles the British used personnel from the Motor Machine Gun Corps, a unit set up in 1915 to man Clyno motor-cycle machine gun combinations for patrol work. The tanks were allocated to a specially formed 'Heavy Branch' of that Corps under Colonel Swinton, the original advocate of tanks for the army.

Tanks were first used in action by the British at Flers–Courcelette in the

closing stages of the Somme offensive, on September 15, 1916, when they were employed (rather prematurely in the opinion of the tank men) to bolster the tail end of an abortive campaign. With limited time for training and small numbers available the tanks were not able to be deployed en masse in the way Colonel Swinton had originally postulated. Thus a possible element of surprise was lost, but this first tank action did bolster flagging morale on the British side. Press reports spoke jubilantly of a tank in the main street of Flers–Courcelette with the British Army cheering behind it. It wasn't quite like this, but the Ministry of Munitions gave its blessing to further orders for tanks and successively improved models, Mks. II, III and IV appeared, the first of the latter being completed in February 1917. All these vehicles retained the rhomboid shape and armament of 'Mother' and Mk. I but there were considerable mechanical refinements in the later vehicles. Also the 'steering tail' was dropped. These tanks all came in two forms – 'Male' with 6 pdr naval gun in each sponson and 'Female' with machine guns in each sponson. They were built in roughly equal numbers, the idea being for the Females to protect the Males from close range infantry attacks. Later there were also 'Hermaphrodites' with one Male and one Female sponson. The sponsons in the Mks. I–III were detachable to reduce the width for travelling by rail or cross-

ing narrow bridges, but a major refinement in the Mk. IV was the provision of smaller sponsons which swung inside the hull instead, so obviating the heavy job of removing and replacing the sponsons.

The next major tank type in British service in 1918 was the Mk. V. This was similar to the Mk. IV but had major mechanical changes in the shape of a specifically designed long stroke Ricardo engine producing 150 hp. New features were external cooling grille and a planetary epicyclic transmission developed by Major Wilson. This made it possible for the driver to control the vehicle single-handed without having to signal to gearsmen or brakemen, so it was a major jump forward. Other major changes included thicker armour, wider tracks, a raised cupola and retractable semaphore arms for signalling to other tanks.

Further improvements were mainly confined to increasing the trench-crossing ability. The first was the 'Tadpole Tail', a tank with lengthened rear horns which increased the ground contact. This idea was dropped because in practice the vehicle lost its stability and the new side pieces lacked rigidity. The problem was solved by the Tank Workshops in France, who in 1918, hit on the idea of breaking a tank in half, inserting three extra side panels and so arriving at a longer vehicle. In this form the vehicle was called the Mk. V★ (stars were used to designate variants).

An added advantage of this con-

A Tank Mk. V*, lengthened to carry troops or stores, with an unditching beam on rails. These were chained to the tracks to provide purchase when the vehicle bogged down.

version was the extra internal stowage volume which was put to good effect to carry stores, or on occasion troops. So successful was the Mk. V* that it was decided to build new vehicles from scratch in Britain. These differed in having the cupola moved forward behind the driver's compartment. They were known as the Mk. V**. Only 25 of these were built and none of them saw war service. At the battle of Amiens in August 1918, Mk. V* tanks were used for the first time to carry infantry forward under armoured protection. This proved none too successful owing to the debilitating effect of the fumes and smoke on the troops inside – on arrival at their destination they were too sick to fight.

Cambrai, November 20, 1917 was the first major battle in which tanks were used in a mass attack in the manner which the early advocates of the 'landships' had envisaged. At Cambrai a huge force of over 450 British tanks was deployed – almost every British tank then in existence. Over a six mile stretch of the line they were to move forward en masse followed up by five infantry divisions. The attack was a brilliant success and clearly vindicated the ideas of those who had fought to get the tank accepted by cavalry-minded generals. An advance of five miles was made, a greater dis-

tance than virtually any previous offensive using infantry and artillery alone. When the British tanks withdrew a German counter attack recovered most of the gains, but the value of the tank was proved once and for all.

A major obstacle to the advance at Cambrai was the formidable Hindenberg line trench system. To cross this the tanks at Cambrai carried cribs of wood, or fascines of brushwood, to drop into the trenches and so form a rudimentary means of crossing the gap. The fascine has remained a common item of tank warfare equipment ever since. Two innovations at Cambrai were wireless tanks – serving as command centres – and supply tanks. Both types were old Mk. Is with armament removed. The supply tanks followed up the battle tanks with ammunition and stores carried in enlarged sponsons. The wireless tanks had offices installed and sported lofty warship style aerial masts.

Other early tank projects in Britain were also of interest as pointers to the future. The so-called Gun Carrier Tank was designed by Tritton using Mk. I automotive parts and was an open-topped vehicle which had a ramp at one end. It carried a 60 pdr field gun or 6 inch howitzer on a 'sledge' which could be run up and down the ramp and emplaced for firing as required. In theory this gave great mobility to the artillery, but its value was not appreciated fully by the artillerymen, so the gun carriers were tactically misused. With

the guns removed the vehicles later gave excellent service as supply tanks.

The 'Flying Elephant' was another Tritton brainchild, an immense mobile fortress with 2 inch armour to withstand German field gun fire. It had four tracks and two Daimler 105 hp engines. The inner pair of tracks could be raised, and brought into use to provide extra traction over rough ground. There were no sponsons, just a nose-mounted 6 pdr and several machine guns. The prototype was nearly completed in 1916 when it was decided to abandon production in favour of standard vehicles. The one and only 'Flying Elephant' was dismantled before it was tested.

The first British departure from the rhomboid shape for tanks was the 'Tritton Chaser' of 1917, later called the 'Whippet' or 'Medium Tank Mk. A'. While the original British tanks were intended to facilitate the advance of infantry and the breakthrough of enemy lines the 'Whippet' was envisaged as a cavalry vehicle able to exploit the piercing of the enemy line. To save weight and give extra speed it had a lowered suspension with a small crew compartment at the rear. Power came from two London bus engines, one driving each track, and the armament was restricted to Hotchkiss machine guns. There was an armoured fuel tank at the front. Steering was achieved by adjusting the engine speed for each track. An order was placed for 200 vehicles in late 1917.

Whippets first went into action in March 1918, and in August 1918 more than 90 were deployed at the battle of Amiens. In practice it was evident that 'cavalry tanks' and horses did not mix, for in this battle the cavalry regiments got too far ahead of the tanks on good going, and fell far behind over rough country. Thereafter the Whippets were used on their own.

They were difficult tanks to drive since the two engines had to be constantly throttled up and down to maintain course. The small driving compartment was hot and cramped.

In the Medium Mark B, the Mk. A's successor, the situation was even worse. This vehicle reverted to the rhomboid shape but as it was small the engines were almost inaccessible and difficult to maintain. Only a few were built but some were sent to Russia – and left there – with the British Expeditionary Force which aided the White Russians in 1919.

The Medium Mk. C came next, a much larger machine which featured the rhomboid shape but had a raised

superstructure and a commander's cupola. Designed by Tritton, it was conceived from the start for mass production. It was made up from sub-assemblies, had plenty of vision ports, a separate engine compartment, and several creature comforts, like food lockers, suggested by experience in the field. It was the finest British tank design of the period and was intended to spearhead the assault in 'Plan 1919', a scheme for a mass tank attack all along the front which Tank Corps staff officers had projected for the spring offensive of 1919. The Armistice in November 1918 ended this notion, and production of the Medium Mk. C, called the 'Hornet', was drastically cut back. The few vehicles completed equipped the small peacetime Tank Corps until about 1926.

Last of the Medium tanks of this era was the Medium Mk. D, a vehicle of great technical sophistication which was designed by a Tank Corps engineer officer, Lt-Col P. Johnson. This tank had a Siddeley Puma aero-engine and articulated flexible 'Snake' tracks which

gave a speed in excess of 20 mph (the Medium Mk. C, by contrast, could achieve 8 mph, and the original Mark I tank only 4 mph). This vehicle was originally intended for use in the great tank breakthrough planned for 1919 and with the Armistice its future became as uncertain as that of other designs. The Mk. D's fate was sealed by its great expense and mechanical complications, and it was cancelled in the early 1920s as an economy move.

From the start of tank operations on the Western Front it soon became apparent that wide ditches could be used to impede the progress of enemy vehicles. The Germans became adept at choosing canals as defence lines or at constructing anti-tank ditches, so that late in 1917 the Tank Corps began to give consideration to means of bridging such obstacles. Though the fascine was an adequate temporary answer to small ditches something better was required. A towed wooden bridge was first evolved, hauled by a tank and man-handled into position. This was impracticable so Major Inglis, a bridging

specialist was called in. He suggested and designed a temporary type of girder bridge, which could be carried slung from hinged king posts on the front of a tank. A winch behind the driving position lowered the bridge into position after which the guys were slipped and the tank backed away.

Three special engineer companies were equipped specially for tank bridge-laying just prior to the Armistice but they were soon disbanded, though a company of bridge-laying tanks was left in the peacetime army. The vehicles used as bridge carriers were the Mk. V**, the factory built version of the Mk. V*, the lengthened version of the Mk. V. In the V** the commander's raised look-out section was moved forward behind the driving cab. The Mk. V**s were used for bridgelaying trials for many years between the wars and at least one was still being used for experimental work in the Second World War. The basic principle for bridge-laying tanks remains virtually unchanged to the present day.

Another novelty of 1918–1919 was the mine clearing tank in which a heavy roller was drawn ahead of the carrying tank to explode mines in the path. This left a 'swept' area for other tanks to follow with immunity from mine damage. Again, this principle established in the First World War has since remained almost unchanged.

German activity in the field of tank development was slow and largely unsuccessful in the 1914–18 period. However, a step forward in armoured vehicle design came with the series of Bremer Marien-Wagons developed in the 1915–1918 period. These were based on Daimler 4 ton trucks which an engineer, H. Bremer, had modified with rudimentary tracks replacing the wheels. Initially tracks were fitted with the normal rear transmission driving the sprockets. The tracks were flimsy affairs with elliptic leaf spring suspension. Further developments were replacement of the front wheels with 'dumb' tracks, used for steering only, and the substitution of a completely armoured body for the lorry body, so

making, in late 1916, the first German full-track armoured vehicle. This was demonstrated to the German General Staff in March 1917 but it failed to impress due to poor traction.

Work on the first tank in Germany did not start until after the first British tanks were encountered. Though spies had reported the building of 'Landships' in Britain, this was not taken seriously. But within a month of the first British tank action the Germans had formed a committee to advise on and design tanks and armoured vehicles. This was the Allgemeine Kriegsdepartment 7, Abteilung Verkehrswesen (War Department 7, Traffic Section), the body responsible for mechanical transport – A7V for short.

The A7V Committee decided to use a Holt tractor chassis which was obtained from the Holt licensees in Austria. This was the best available chassis that could be adapted without extensive development. Main work on the A7V tank was done by an engineer, Joseph Vollmer. His initial design con-

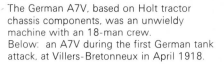

sisted of an armoured hull over a basic Holt chassis, but the vehicle was never built in this form. Instead the chassis was lengthened and with it the hull so that more guns could be accommodated. In the A7V two Daimler 100 bhp engines were placed centrally, with the driver and commander above them in a raised cupola. This position had duplicate controls for driving in either direction. The box-like hull had a Russian Sokol 57 mm gun at the front with two machine guns each side and two at the rear. The vehicle had armour 20–30 mm thick and a crew of 18. One hundred A7Vs were ordered

in the middle of 1917, but there were considerable delays due to inadequate production facilities and a shortage of armour plate. The armour itself was of low quality and later vehicles had one-piece sides instead of plates in an attempt to give added strength.

Only about 20 A7Vs were actually completed as tanks but chassis production continued. In late 1917 30 of the completed chassis were converted to A7V Uberlandwagen cross-country vehicles by the addition of a cab over the engine section and dropside bodies at each end. These were used as supply carriers in 1918.

As a tank the A7V was a failure, for it had the inherent faults of low track vehicles: it was unstable and had poor trench-crossing capabilities due to the overhang of the body. By contrast, the British tanks with all-round tracks and low centre of gravity could more easily surmount obstacles and extricate themselves from ditches – the unditch-ing beam, chained to the tracks was useful here.

The first German action with A7V tanks took place at St Quentin on March 21st 1918 when the first two companies (formed in December 1917) were deployed. The most successful tanks used by the Germans, however, were ex-British Mk IVs captured at the Battle of Cambrai and re-armed with German guns. Ironically enough the bulk of the German tank forces was made up from captured British tanks, mainly Mk IVs and Whippets re-armed with German guns.

In 1915 there was a wave of interest in France in producing vehicles suitable for use in trench warfare conditions. Early ideas concentrated on adapting agricultural tractors with cutters and rollers to penetrate barbed wire. Holt tractors were also purchased and one of these was armoured and demonstrated to the President of France and senior army officials in June 1915. While this armoured Holt was limited in performance it lead to a request to the firm of Schneider to make a study for the design of a proper armoured vehicle.

Meanwhile an imaginative infantry officer, Colonel Estienne, had been pressing for 'armoured tractors' for many months and he eventually saw the French C-in-C, Foch, to explain his ideas in person. Foch was keen and this lead to Estienne co-operating with Schneider in designing the tank which had already been ordered. Ten Schneider tanks were ordered in December 1915. This was soon increased to 400, all to be delivered by November 1916. The finalised Schneider design was closely derived from the original Holt tractor, utilising a Holt-type chassis but with armoured suspension beams. The driver sat in the front of a box-like body with a 75 mm machine gun to the right and machine guns each side. The overall design was poor, however, compared with the British tanks. In particular, side-mounted fuel tanks were a severe fire hazard and losses in action were heavy. There were many production delays, and by April 1917 only just half the order was complete. It was in this month that the first French tank attack took place near Chemin des Dames. Later, Schneider tank production tailed off in favour of artillery and supply tractors on the same chassis.

The second major French heavy tank of this period was the St Chamond, a 'rival' design to the Schneider. This was evolved by the Mechanical Transport Service, which was annoyed that Colonel Estienne had managed to get a

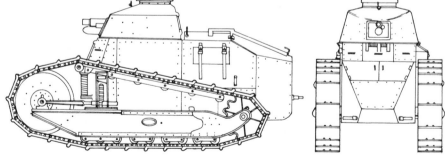

Early French types. the Schneider (top) and St. Chamond (centre) were based on the Holt chassis; the St. Chamond stuck in a ditch by its nose demonstrates inherent faults of this low type of chassis, its overhanging superstructure.
Bottom: the Renault FT light tank, an outstanding First World War design.

tank into production by by-passing the normal bureaucratic War Office channels. Novel features of the vehicle included petrol-electric drive with an electric motor for each track, and the use of two Holt suspension units which gave an extra set of bogies each side and so lengthened ground contact. A 75 mm gun, derived from the famous French field gun, was fitted in the nose and there were three Hotchkiss machine guns, one also in the nose. The long box-like hull overhung the chassis considerably at each end. In April 1916 400 St Chamond tanks were ordered and the first were in service in May 1917. Due to the long overhang at both nose and tail these vehicles very easily became stranded and like all other Holt-based vehicles were top heavy and unstable. The St Chamond was even more vulnerable than the Schneider though its armament and mechanical features were superior.

Some St Chamonds had the gun removed and were used as supply tanks.

The Germans effectively countered the Holt-chassis French tanks in 1917 by widening their trenches so that attacking vehicles were stuck down by their overhanging noses. It was the adoption of the 'all round' track on British tanks by contrast that gave the British a decisive lead in tank technology in the early days.

Renault had been approached with the idea of tank production in 1915 but the famous French firm was then too busy with other war production to get involved with tank development. In July 1916 Colonel Estienne, now commander of the French tank forces, approached Renault again, this time to make a very light tank for the use of force commanders and also to act as a machine gun support vehicle for the infantry. This led to the development of the Renault FT (sometimes called

A Renault FT disarmed and used by the British as a liaison vehicle, Western Front, 1918. There were many variants of this famous tank, which saw service in many parts of the world.

the Mosquito), one of the most important of all early designs. Designed by Estienne, it weighed less than 5 tons so that it could be carried by truck or trailer for speedy deployment, and to conserve its track life, a perpetual hazard for early tanks which were often disabled simply by track breakage. The Renault was the first vehicle to adopt the 'modern' tank type of layout with traversing turret, rear engine and a raised superstructure. Similarly it dispensed with a chassis, the hull forming the main strength section of the vehicle. The track arrangement, well forward of the hull front, reduced the chances of bogging down by the nose while a

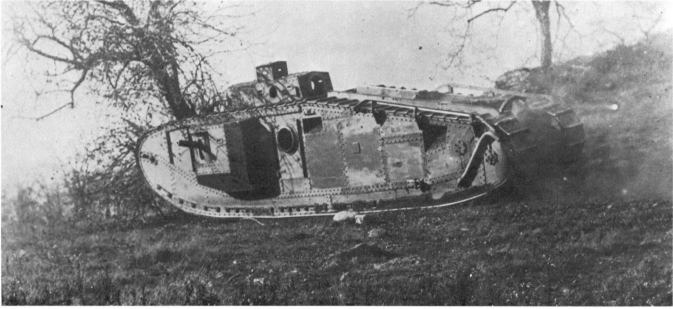

removable 'tail' of girders at the rear increased the effective length. In May 1917, after successful prototype trials, 1,000 Renaults were ordered, later increased by 3,500. Soon a whole production group of firms was set up to make Renaults in the numbers required. The FT17 became numerically the most important French tank of the First World War, and the most widely used. It was employed in its command and liaison role by the British, and became a favourite mount for tank battalion commanders and staff officers.

After the War Renaults were sold to (or copied by) numerous governments, and Renaults or Renault copies served in Russia, China, Japan, Italy, Spain, Hungary and Belgium. There were still some in French service in 1940 and some of these were subsequently cap-

tured and used by the Germans – 25 years after their introduction.

There were numerous production variants of the Renault FT, including a command tank (Renault TSF) with enlarged superstructure replacing the turret. There was the inevitable 'Char Cargo' which had built up superstructure and a loading ramp, while there were various self-propelled gun models including a 75 mm SP gun on the FT chassis which was built experimentally in 1918. The gun faced the rear (due to the engine position) with a platform for the gunners between the front horns. It was abandoned after the Armistice of November 1918.

Meanwhile Germany concentrated on the heavy A7V tanks and an even bigger vehicle was evolved, the K-Wagen, a 148-ton monster with a 22

man crew and four 7·7 cm guns; it was designed to take apart for road or rail transport. This was such a big project that the prototype was still incomplete when Germany surrendered. At the other extreme Joseph Vollmer, who had designed the A7V, championed the idea of simple light tanks. He designed a small tank called the Leichte Kampfwagen (light combat vehicle) I which was based on a Mercedes car chassis and was not unlike the British Whippet in external size and shape. It was, however, much less sophisticated mechanically, using the normal drive and transmission of the Mercedes. The LKI impressed the German War Office who based a formal specification on it, calling for a 57 mm gun armament and for thicker armour. This led to the LKII, a vehicle similar to its predecessor

except for a fixed rear barbette to carry the heavier gun. In June 1918 an order for 580 LKII was placed but none was completed before the Armistice. A further projected development was the LKIII, virtually the LKI back-to-front with the engine forward and the gun aft.

Yet another prototype completed was a Krupp light tank which was novel in having a height of just over 5 ft, a machine gun in the nose, and a large shield at the back intended to protect following infantry. This ideal little vehicle for trench warfare conditions was not put into production before the Armistice.

The faults of the A7V tanks were realised as soon as they entered service. The advantage of the rhomboid shape and overall tracks of the British tanks

became apparent from testing captured vehicles. To succeed the A7V therefore the A7V Committee decided to produce an exact copy of the British Mk IV tank, but on further consideration this was seen to be impractical due to the stringent economic conditions in Germany, which in 1918 was suffering the full effects of the blockade. Vollmer, the A7V designer, therefore did the next best thing and built a rhomboidal tank based on the existing A7V components. Mechanically the new vehicle was the same as A7V, complete with twin Daimler engines and Holt suspension. Superficially the shape resembled the British tanks. The new vehicle was called the A7V/U (U standing for Umlanfende Ketten, or circumrotatory tracks). Two 57 mm Sokol guns were carried in the side

sponsons. The vehicle had a top speed of 7½ mph. Only the prototype was completed, in June 1918, and although 20 more were ordered, none was completed by November 1918 when the Armistice put an end to the war. Thus ended Germany's somewhat slow and uncertain start with armoured fighting vehicles.

America entered the war in April 1917 and the formation of an American Tank Corps was announced in the following September. It was planned to have five heavy and 20 light battalions in France, with further battalions training in America. The heavy battalions were trained by the British and equipped with British Mk IV and Mk V tanks. The light battalions had the French Renault FT tanks and were trained and equipped in France. The Renault FT was adopted for production in America, where it was modified to suit American production standards, fitted with a Buda engine, and known as the M1917 or 'Six Tonner'. In 1940, incidentally, some surviving vehicles of this type were handed to the Canadians as 'stop gaps' while new tanks were built in Canada.

For the American heavy battalions it was decided to use the latest British design, the Mark VIII, on which work started in mid-1917. This vehicle incorporated all the lessons learned from previous tank experience on the Western Front and was a considerable advance on all the previous heavy designs. Features included lengthened ground contact, wider tracks, raised cupola for the driver and commander,

Tank attack. British tanks approaching the
German trenches over 'No Man's Land' on
the Western Front in 1917.

all-round machine gun coverage and a
separate engine room. The Americans
supplied a production engineer to join
the British designers to advise on mass-
production modifications. In late 1917
a grandiose formal plan was drawn up
to produce the Mark VIII jointly with
the USA and France as a standard
Allied heavy tank. The ambassadors of
Britain, France and America signed an
Anglo-American Tank Treaty em-
bodying the plan in their respective
countries. From this treaty the vehicle
later became known as the 'International' tank. It was also called the
'Liberty' tank after its proposed American engine. A special factory was to be
built for production of 1,500 Mark
VIII vehicles in France and each country
also made plans for home production.
Price per tank was to be £5,000. However, French interest in the project
evaporated at an early date and there
were severe delays in building the
French factory, which was still incomplete in November 1918 when the

Armistice was signed. As a result
Britain also ceased building the tanks
and only prototype Mk VIII tanks
were completed. The British vehicles
had Rolls-Royce engines. Construction was subsequently confined only to
100 tanks in America from parts
already in hand. These Mk VIIIs formed the main American tank strength
from completion in 1919 until 1932.
They were then stored and saw service
again in 1940 when they were handed
over to the infant Canadian Tank
Corps as training vehicles while tank
production got under way in Canada.

Meanwhile numerous tank projects
were put forward in America, every-
thing from armoured tractors to a
steam-propelled vehicle based broadly
on British designs. Of these the major
type, and the only one to see production, was the Ford two-man tank
which was designed by the Ordnance
Department utilising Ford Model T
automobile parts. It weighed only 3
tons and was to be built by the Ford
Motor Co to supplement the Renault
FT. The two man crew sat in front with
a driver to the right and gunner to the
left. The two Model T engines gave a
top speed of 8 mph, and drove through

Model T gearboxes, one to each track.
Orders for over 15,000 of these vehicles
were placed but only 15 were built
since production was cancelled after
the Armistice. The few existing
vehicles were sent to France in late 1918
and were generally used to tow guns
and stores trailers. They never saw
action. A bigger Ford tank was also
designed, with three-man crew and
turret, but it was not proceeded with
after 1918.

Among the more exotic American
tank designs of 1917–18 were such
oddities as the Skeleton Tank which
had a rhomboid shape made entirely
in metal tubing and had a fighting and
engine compartment suspended in the
frame work. There were several designs based on the inevitable Holt
tractor, two of them made by Holt
themselves and almost exactly like
Colonel Swinton's original conception
of 1915. A Holt gas-electric tank showed promise as, indeed, did the curious
steam tank which was financed by
some American industrialists. However, all these projects foundered in the
desire to standardise with America's
more experienced Allies, France and
Britain, in this field.

BETWEEN THE WARS

The 1920s started inevitably with a rapid run-down in military forces and their equipment. German military activity was severely curtailed by the Treaty of Versailles and her limited armed forces were allowed only a few armoured cars for internal security duties (although in fact some secret studies of armoured vehicles were made, which later led to prototypes).

France had such a large stock of tanks left from the war years that no real attempts were made to build replacement vehicles until about 1930, when a whole new family of well designed tanks started to appear.

Major French efforts in the 1920s

The Russian BA-32, based on a truck chassis and mounting a 45 mm gun. These vehicles served throughout the Second World War — this photograph was taken in 1943.

were confined to completing some giant 'breakthrough' tanks which had been started in 1918 when the race for monster impregnable 'landships' was just getting under way. Germany was then building the K-Wagen and under pressure from the artillerists of the 'Artillerie d'Assaut' the French High Command agreed to the construction of a monster gas-electric 42 tonner with a 105 mm gun. Construction of a small number of such heavy tanks was authorised and these were eventually completed after the war. The first design, the Char 1A eventually weighed in at 50 tons, and was 30 ft long. Its frontal armour was 1·4 in. thick, and the sides ·64 in. Later the 105 mm gun was changed to a 75 mm weapon in the interests of standardisation. An improved model was the Char 2C, a

multi-turret machine with a forward 75 mm gun and machine guns in the rear turret and hull sides. It was 33 ft long, weighed over 74 tons, and had twin Renault engines of 500 bhp, giving a top road speed of only 4 mph. Last of this line was the Char 3C, built in small numbers in 1929. It retained the previous armament but had added machine guns. It was over 39 ft long and weighed about 80 tons; its triple engines, totalling 1,980 bhp brought the speed up to 8 mph. An attempt was made to use these vulnerable vehicles in the face of the German advance in 1940, but they were destroyed in air attacks while in transit to the front.

In Russia the Soviet authorities made their first attempts to build up armoured forces. At this time Russia was a very backward country in in-

Left: Medium Tank T1 of 1927-29, later
designated Medium Tank M1, and (below)
Light Tank T1E1, one of a series of American
light tank prototypes of the early 1930s.
Right: the British Medium Tank Mk.II,
distinguished from the Mk.I by the armour
covers over the suspension. Note the
'bishop's mitre' type cupola hatch for the
commander.

in 1920 a National Defense Act made tanks an infantry responsibility, under the pretext that the 'main function of the tank was to facilitate the advance of the infantryman in the attack'. This, in effect, was a restatement of the original conception of tanks, and thus the 1920 Defense Act led to the abolition of the Tank Corps and tanks became very much a 'Cinderella' in the infantry's list of peacetime priorities. Some prototypes of the immediate post-war period, the M1921 and M1922, designed before the Act, were completed, but none was taken up, for a 1921 infantry review of tanks re-stated requirements as being for a truck-transportable 5 ton light tank – i.e., the American version of the Renault FT, the M1917 – and a 15 ton medium tank, this being the maximum weight then permitted on existing army bridging equipment. The M1921 and its derivatives all weighed over this limit.

In the rest of the 1920s period no more significant work was done on tank development until the T2 medium tank appeared in 1929–30, built to the 15 ton weight limit. In 1928 a T1 light tank also appeared, but this was little more than a tractor type of chassis with a turret and 37 mm gun. By 1931 several further developments had appeared, T1E1, T1E2, and T1E3, all successively improved prototypes. They had two man crews and Cunningham V-8 engines giving a top speed of about 20 mph. They were just over $12\frac{1}{2}$ ft long and 7 ft high. None saw production.

A vehicle on a similar chassis was the T1 Howitzer Motor Carriage, a 75 mm howitzer in a limited traverse mount. Again it was a prototype only, typical of those financially stringent times,

dustrial terms so the few indigenous designs which appeared were not taken up. The Red Army in the 1920-22 period had a motley collection of tanks which had been captured from (or left behind by) the Allied Expeditionary Force which aided the White Russians. Ex-British Mk V tanks and Whippets, and French Renault FT tanks were the main vehicles, and the Soviets found the answer to their tank problem in taking the simplest design and copying.

This gave rise to the vehicle which was popularly called the 'Russki-Renault'. In most respects it was like the original vehicle, but in improved model, the MS-1 and MS-2 of 1928, there were mechanical changes, and a lengthened hull.

This notion of copying foreign designs lent itself admirably to Russia's industrial situation and the practice was

followed right up to the Second World War, almost every vehicle type being a licence-built version of a British, French, or American machine, with Russian ideas incorporated. American technical aid resulted in the building of a factory for licence-production of Ford Model A automobiles and trucks in the late 1920s, and this in turn led to the appearance of several armoured car types in the early 1930s. These were based on Ford truck chassis and engines. Popularly known as 'Broniefords' the two major models were the BA7 and BA32, crude in appearance but fast, well-armoured and effective. They were used through the Second World War.

In America the armoured forces fared badly in the 1920s, with only the 100 Mark VIII 'Liberty' tanks being of any significant value. But

when for years the only new tanks built in America were one-off prototypes.

Britain's commanding lead in tank development in the 1916–18 period was largely frittered away by a combination of apathy, indecision and financial stringency. As elsewhere, there were massive cuts in the armed services and many of the most experienced Tank Corps men were demobilised. Money available for expenditure on new armaments was negligible, in the assumption that there would be no major war for some time. Above all, very little was deduced by the General Staff from the use of tanks in the war, except that they were vaguely useful. Few senior Tank Corps officers remained in positions influential enough to further the cause of the tank and there was something of a return to outmoded pre-war ideas of the value of cavalry.

After the sophisticated and costly Medium Mk D tank was abandoned, consideration was given instead in 1921 to a much cheaper design, the Vickers Light Tank. This followed the rhomboidal shape and layout of the Medium Mk B and C but instead of a fixed superstructure it had a rotating turret. Two prototypes were built, one with three Hotchkiss machine guns and another with a 3 pdr gun and an AA machine gun. These vehicles were tested by the army in 1921–22 but were not adopted. However, Vickers used the experience to build a new tank very similar in layout to the 1921 design but with features suggested by the Tank Corps after the official tests.

The new vehicle appeared in 1923 as the Light Tank Mk 1 until in the following year it was reclassified Medium Tank Mk 1 when some even lighter tanks appeared. This basic design proved most successful and it

was followed in 1925 by the Medium Tank Mk II which was basically similar to the Mk I but had a bulkier hull, armoured covers over the spring bogie suspension, and numerous small detail changes. They were roomy vehicles, well liked by their crews and very dependable. The Mk I and II tanks formed the backbone of Britain's Tank Corps in the inter-war years, about 200 vehicles being built in all, including many variants. They were in service until 1938, then soldiered on into the Second World War as training vehicles. One or two were still in use defending Tobruk in 1942.

The Dragon Mk I of 1922 was not strictly speaking from the same parentage as the Medium Mk I tank but had a similar chassis, tracks, suspension and mechanical layout and was designed at the same time. This open topped vehicle was intended to haul 18 pdr field guns in place of the horse teams

The Valentine tank, or Infantry Tank Mk.III was
designed and built by Vickers (the design
was submitted to the War Office on St.
Valentine's Day, 1938, hence the name
chosen for the vehicle). It was a good design
though limited by its small size which
restricted its development potential. First
vehicles were in service in 1940 and the type
was used in the Western Desert. Nearly 1,500
were built in Canada and most of these were
given to Russia under Lease-Lend arrangements. British factories built another 8,275.
The Mk.I model, shown here, had the 2pdr
gun but subsequent models mounted the
6 pdr (Valentine VIII, IX and X) and 75 mm
gun (Mk.XI). Armour maximum was 65 mm
and speed was 15 mph.

Right and opposite top: The Infantry Tank
Mk.IV was better known as the Churchill. The
Churchill II, shown here, was one of the
early models, in service in 1941–42. The shape
was reminiscent of First World War tanks and
the design originated from a 1939
requirement for a 'shelled area' tank for the
Western Front. Though dogged by early
mechanical troubles the Churchill proved to
be one of the best British tanks. Its regular
shape lent itself to adaptation for special
purpose requirements, dozens of Churchill
variants being built (altogether 5,600
vehicles were built). The Mk.II version had
the 2 pdr gun, weighed $38\frac{1}{2}$ tons, was $24\frac{1}{2}$ ft
long and had 102 mm armour maximum. A
Bedford 350 hp engine gave a speed of 15
mph.

previously used. 'Dragon', incidentally, was a corruption of 'Drag Gun'. The Dragon had a normal commercial 60 bhp Leyland truck engine and was inadequately powered. An improved model, the Dragon Mk II, was duly produced with shielded sides, 'skirts' over the suspension, and a more powerful 82 bhp Armstrong Siddeley air-cooled engine, which was also used in the Mk I and II tanks. Britain was early to mechanise its artillery in this way – many other nations were still using horses in 1939.

The Dragon Mk I formed the basis for one of the earliest bridge-carrier tanks in 1923–25. A simple box-like superstructure supported a girder bridge, launched along a pair of steel runners which were projected forward over the gap to be spanned. This was never advanced past the experimental stage. A lighter type of girder bridge was similarly fitted to a Medium Mk II tank, again only experimentally.

Another British innovation in the mid-1920s period was the idea of highly mobile tracked self-propelled guns. These were built by Vickers, again on similar chassis to the Medium tanks and were called 'Birch Guns' (after the name of the then Master General of the Ordnance who postulated the idea). The prototype vehicle appeared in 1925 and four slightly

improved vehicles were put into service in 1926. The gun was a standard 18 pdr suitable for ground or anti aircraft fire. In the latter role it could be used with a predictor operating from an accompanying vehicle. In 1928 two further improved vehicles were built, this time with a full armoured barbette. The gun in this design however, could only be used for ground fire. Although the Birch Gun was advanced in concept no more were built, partly from lack of funds and partly due to the mechanical limitations of the chassis.

By 1927 an experimental 'Mechan-

A Medium Mk.II command tank, specially equipped for the commander of the Experimental Mechanised Force in 1927, leading other medium tanks of the force on summer manoeuvres on Salisbury Plain. Opposite: the A6, which was to have been the Medium Tank Mk.III. With a 3 pdr main gun and twin auxiliary machine gun turrets, the A6 was a major design advance.

ised Force' had been formed which was virtually the prototype for the armoured divisions adopted by all major armies in later years. It was the brainchild of Capt Liddell-Hart, Colonel Fuller, and others who had tank experience in the First World

War. Liddell-Hart had been an infantry officer who turned journalist and was the most influential defence writer of the inter-war period. His ideas – and those of others with an interest in tanks – were well publicised in his writings and many of his theories were realised by the armoured division system of the Second World War. Ironically the most enthusiastic students

The A1 'Independent' was a big 30 ton machine with four auxiliary turrets which never saw production. Here it exercises with a Carden-Loyd tankette (right) and a Morris-Martel tankette (in the distance).

of his work were the Germans, and several famous tank generals of the Second World War, notably Guderian and Rommel, were greatly influenced by Liddell-Hart's ideas. In Britain, however, Liddell-Hart was something of a 'prophet without honour' for his views were either rejected or simply not heeded by the General Staff, particularly in the early 1930s when Britain's tank strength was at a low ebb.

The 'Mechanised Force' in 1927 nevertheless had a balanced allocation of medium and light armoured vehicles, plus lorried infantry and the

Birch Guns. For the next few years, until dispersed as a defence economy, the 'Mechanised Force' was the showpiece of the British Army and tried out and evolved some of the tank tactics used subsequently in the Second World War. A Medium Mk II tank was specially adapted as a command vehicle in 1928 for the tank brigade commander, complete with roomy box body to give space for wireless sets, map tables, and staff officers.

To replace the Medium Mk II, a greatly improved vehicle, the A6 appeared in 1929. This had a lower superstructure, rear mounted engine, a 3 pdr gun in the turret, and two auxiliary machine gun turrets in front. Three production vehicles (differing in detail) designated Medium Mk III, were completed in 1930, but no more of these relatively expensive machines were built. The Medium Mk III was important, however, since it established the general physical lay-out of all subsequent British medium-sized tanks. It also inspired the designs of similar types built in Germany, Russia and Japan.

The most notable and impressive of British tank designs between the wars was the very fine A1, or 'Independent', a very large vehicle which owed something to the French 'break-through' tanks already described. Like them it

Right: the Crusader Mk.I, which had a 2 pdr gun and an auxiliary machine gun turret, was the fastest British tank of its time and was best known for its part in the Western Desert fighting of 1941–42. This model weighed 19 tons, had a crew of five, a top speed of 27 mph, 40 mm armour (maximum) and was 19 ft 8 in long. A close-support model had a 3 inch howitzer instead of a 2 pdr gun.

Right below: the big Boarhound armoured car was built specially for the desert war but the fighting in North Africa had ceased by the time it was ready. The Boarhound weighed 23·6 tons, had a top speed of 50 mph and a 6 pdr gun with stabiliser. It was virtually a wheeled tank. Built in America to British requirements it was one of the largest armoured cars ever designed.

Opposite: a German PzKmpfw IV Ausf D, the largest German tank in general service in 1940, and one of the few tanks to stay in production and service throughout the Second World War. This close view shows the commander in his vision cupola wearing the style of tank crew service dress of the time. The beret covers a close fitting protective helmet. The radio aerial was designed to fold into the adjacent channelling when the turret traversed.

was a multi-turret design with a 3 pdr gun in a main turret and four auxiliary machine gun turrets. It was fast for its size, comfortable and well armoured. It inspired the heavy Russian tanks of the 1930s, which were quite similar in appearance and layout.

The 'Independent' was thought of as a 'battleship' or 'capital' tank, to use a nautical analogy which was then fashionable; tank battles were envisaged in the future where 'fleets' of tanks manoeuvred and fought like battle fleets at sea – the possible effects of the fledgling air forces and artillery bombardments were conveniently forgotten. The 'Independent' followed the fate of so many other designs of the time. It was too expensive to produce and only the prototype was built (and it exists to this day).

In the 1920s, financial stringency led directly to the small infantry carrier, which was to become a major type of vehicle in the Second World War and which has evolved subsequently into the sophisticated armoured carriers of the 1970s. A Tank Corps officer, Colonel G. Le Q. Martel, proposed small, cheap armoured vehicles, able to carry an infantryman and his machine gun safely across open country. To prove his point, Martel built a prototype of the thing he had in mind, utilising rubber tracks in conjunction with a car type chassis. One further idea was that this so called 'tankette' also had a commercial potential as a light agricultural tractor; this does not appear to have been followed up, although the motoring journals of the day illustrated tankettes towing ploughs. The wide Press publicity when the tankette appeared led to a trial order for some vehicles of this type, which were built by Morris Motors, largely to Martel's original design. The new vehicles were subsequently used in the Mechanised Force of 1927, where they proved useful in a reconnaisance role rather than for the intended purpose as personal mounts for individual infantrymen.

Meanwhile Mr John Carden of Loyd's Garage had similar ideas and was building a small tankette on the same general lines as Martel's. His designs, the Carden-Loyd Mk I and Mk II, were fully tracked, the latter model having auxiliary side and steering wheels.. Subsequent models had

lower bathlike bodies and eight of these (in their more advanced Mk V form) were used by the British Army in the 1927 Mechanised Force trials alongside the Morris-Martel machines. As a result of these trials a production order was given to Carden-Loyd, which had meanwhile been taken over by Vickers. The finalised design, the Carden-Loyd Mk VI had an enlarged hull, was powered by a Ford Model T engine, and was lightly armoured. The wheeled carriage was dispensed with and the vehicle ran only on its tracks. The two man crew – a driver and a gunner – sat each side of the engine and a Vickers machine gun was arranged to fire for-

ward (the gun could be demounted).

The Carden-Loyd Mk. VI was the first true infantry carrier and it served through the 1930s in many roles, for example as a mortar carrier, infantry gun tractor, anti-tank gun tractor and smoke layer. It could also tow tracked trailers carrying infantrymen or stores.

The Carden-Loyd was a hugely successful design which had a great influence on contemporary AFV development. Commercial variants built by Vickers were sold all over the world; some nations built them under licence and others merely copied the layout and style. Portugal, Japan, China, Italy, Russia, Poland, Bolivia,

Opposite, top: the Carden-Loyd Mk.IV tankette was an important vehicle in the evolution of the machine gun carrier. One of the designs which it inspired was the Renault UE infantry carrier (below).
Above: the Light Dragon Mk.II, here towing a 4·5 inch howitzer, was a further step in the development of the infantry carrier. This vehicle was still in service in the first years of the Second World War.
Below: the Bren Gun Carrier, developed from earlier Vickers and Carden-Loyd vehicles, was a major type in service until 1942. These are Australian-manned carriers in Malaya in 1941.

Belgium, Chile, Holland, Czecho-slovakia and Siam were principal buyers. A major user, Russia, copied the design (after purchasing some) and called it the T-27. France built a similar close copy, the Renault UE which had dome type head covers.

In 1934 Vickers improved on their own design by developing a longer chassis with the stronger Horstmann sprung suspension which formed the basis for a larger and much sturdier infantry carrier. Offered with a 40 mm gun as a self propelled artillery piece

the design attracted the attention of the War Office, which ordered prototypes for the machine gun carrier and gun tractor ('Light Dragon') roles. This design overcame the main limitation of the Carden-Loyd, inadequate carry-ing capacity. Aside from the crew the new vehicle, Carrier Machine Gun No 1, Mk I, could carry two men each side of the engine which was fitted behind the front fighting compart-ment. An improved design (Carrier No 2, Mk I), quickly followed, this having a front barbette for the Vickers

machine gun and a full-width fighting compartment.

The most famous development in the Vickers carrier series, was the well-known Bren Gun Carrier. This was evolved in 1937 specifically to equip infantry battalions as a carrying vehicle for the Bren light machine gun which was then on issue as an infantry platoon weapon. The Bren Carrier had a three man crew, a Ford 65 bhp engine and a top speed of 30 mph. It was essentially similar to the old machine gun carrier but had a shaped front barbette and superior crew protection.

Other carrier variants of the 1937–1940 period were the Cavalry Carrier and Scout Carrier. These were mechanically similar to the Bren Carrier but had different layouts for the special roles. The Cavalry Carrier was intended to transport the personnel of mechanised cavalry regiments. However, only a few were made, for the other carrier types could carry out this role quite adequately. The Scout Carrier was a reconnaissance vehicle for light tank regiments. It had its rear passenger compartment on the opposite side to the Bren Carrier. It was equipped with a Boys anti-tank rifle, a Bren gun on an AA mount and a 3 inch smoke projector.

During the Second World War the need for a new carrier design which could carry out all the roles which had previously been performed by specialised types was soon realised. It had to be used by infantry, tank, and other arms, carrying or towing a variety of guns. So evolved the Universal Carrier. To supplement the Vickers design of Universal Carrier there appeared the Loyd Carrier, designed by Vivian Loyd; this was a very simple design using readily available Ford commercial parts. Horstmann suspension, a canvas tilt, and a basic unarmoured hull (to which armour plates could be fixed) were features of the design. The Loyd Carrier was used in various secondary roles, for example as a telegraph line layer, but was mainly employed to tow anti-tank guns in infantry service.

The Universal Carrier still suffered from being too small, so when carrier production became fully established in Canada during the Second World War a lengthened version of the original design was produced which gave more storage space, for roles like mortar carrying or anti-tank gun towing. This Canadian design of 1944 was called the Windsor Carrier. A very similar design was built for Britain in America at the same time, under the U.S. designation Carrier T16. These types had a long military career, some being still in service in 1960.

In the field of conventional tank development, Vickers became one of the leaders in the 1930s and their designs sold overseas in quantity, were licence built in some countries, and influenced many contemporary designs elsewhere. Vickers' two most significant tanks were the Vickers Light Tank Mk I (the British Army designation) which appeared in 1929 and the 6 tonner of 1930.

The Light Tank Mk I was developed from the Carden-Loyd tankettes, having a slightly larger hull and Horst-

The Light Tank Mk.I of 1929 was the fore-runner of a whole family of British Light tanks.

mann leaf spring suspension, plus a simple machine gun turret and 14 mm armour maximum. It had a top speed of 30 mph and weight was 2½ tons. An improved model produced in 1930 was designated the Mk IA. This had coil spring suspension and better armour disposition. The Mk II of 1931 was similar again but had a larger turret and a better engine. These models were considerably developed in the next decade and the light tank, which was inexpensive and ideal for colonial policing, became the principal British tank type. Germany and Japan were among the countries which purchased examples of these vehicles and used features of them in their own light tank designs.

The other Vickers design was not adopted by the British Army but had a major influence on tank development elsewhere. This was the Vickers 6 Ton Tank, a very successful and reliable design which was sold commercially

The Vickers 6 ton Tank Type A was not used by the British Army, but was widely exported.

overseas. There were two main models, Type A with twin turrets mounting machine guns and Type B with a single turret and 47 mm (3 pdr) gun. Customers for this vehicle included Russia, Holland, Thailand, Portugal, Poland, Bolivia, Rumania, Greece, Estonia, China and Argentina. The vehicle was compact, simple in layout and reasonably fast at 22 mph. The basic design, but with a heavier suspension was subsequently developed into what became the M2 and M3 series of light tanks in America in 1938–41.

In America between the wars a major innovator in the field of tank design was J. Walter Christie, an automotive engineer who became involved in producing armoured vehicles in the First World War. Christie's work had a profound influence on Russian and British tank development, although little in his native land. His first designs, in 1916–18, were concerned with the carriages for self-propelled guns. Early self-propelled guns were under-powered and usually unstable. Christie used big wheels with long-stroke spring suspension, long

pitch tracks, and powerful engines. His few successful early designs impressed the US Army and Christie persuaded them to give him a contract for a tank based on the self-propelled gun chassis. This design, the M1919, was unsatisfactory, in part because it was underpowered, and it was reconstructed as the M1921 light tank, with extra road wheels to improve its performance and a hull-mounted gun instead of a turret originally used. By this time American defence spending had been drastically reduced following the Armistice, and official interest in the project, as in many others, ended.

Meanwhile the inventive Christie had built a tracked amphibious carrier or tank and had perfected his suspension system. On a chassis with four large road wheels each side the rear three wheels were each carried on long stroke spring axles with vertical play in each wheel. The leading pair of wheels was sprung horizontally and these wheels were carried on forward projecting arms which pivoted for steering. In Christie's system there were front idlers, and rear sprocket wheels driven from the engine.

Christie's idea was for a very fast high-powered vehicle which could run on tracks or, when conditions allowed, run on its road wheels like an armoured car. Although Christie had no official sponsorship he built a vehicle to this conception which was offered for military trials in 1928 when the Americans were following the British scheme of organising a 'Mechanised Force' with a nucleus of tanks and mobile infantry. The M1928 (as the vehicle was designated by Christie) was finally tested in 1930 and a small production order was placed, under the official designation Medium Tank T3. The vehicle, with a 37 mm gun was the first tank produced in any numbers (about 35) since the Mk VIII tanks of 1919–20. Two men could remove or replace the tracks in 30 minutes and the tracks were stowed on the track covers. A modified aero engine, a Liberty 338 bhp V-12 and a weight of 10.5 tons gave a high power to weight ratio, and the top speed of the T3 was over 27 mph, which was very high for the period. A development of the T3 was the M1931 which was adopted by the US Cavalry as the T1 Combat Car. The term 'combat car' was a legal way of evading the 1920 Defense Act, and when the US cavalry realised the need for tanks to take over

the scouting role from horsed squadrons, they got their demands passed in 1930 by calling their vehicles 'combat cars'.

The US Army did not pursue development of the Christie tank to any great extent, and it was left to the Soviet Army to fully exploit its potential. In 1931 Russia purchased two T3 vehicles and acquired a production licence. In Russia the vehicle was dubbed the Bystrochodya Tank (fast tank) or BT by virtue of its high speed. A series of Russian development models appeared from 1931 until 1937, the early marks having a 400 bhp copy of the Liberty engine and the BT-5 onwards having a modified Russian aero engine. The first major Russian production type was the BT-2 of 1932 which had a new Russian designed turret with 37 mm gun. In 1935–36 an improved model, the BT-7, appeared with a greatly enlarged turret, and a 45 mm gun. In this vehicle the weight was increased and the facility for running on wheels was discontinued as, in practice, it was little used.

The one remaining type of British tank developed in the 1930s was the so-called 'infantry tank'. This was actually a refinement of the original idea of the tank, which was to *support* an infantry advance. British tank doc-

Christie's M1931 was one of a series of similar models and one of the few to see US Army service, where it was designated T3. This trio are running on wheels, with tracks stowed on hull sides.

trine of the early 1930s postulated three types of vehicle – light tanks for scouting, medium (later cruiser) tanks moving in 'fleets' to engage enemy tanks, and infantry tanks to punch holes in an enemy line for the infantry to follow. The infantry tank was heavily armoured to withstand enemy shellfire and it only needed to move at infantry pace – walking speed. The design of the first infantry tank, the A11 (named the Matilda for its duck-like gait), was carried out by Vickers in 1934 to a strict budget. Production started in 1938 and vehicles of this type were in service in France with the British Expeditionary Force (B.E.F.) in 1940. The Matilda or Infantry Tank Mk I was small, just 16 ft long and 6 ft 1½ in high. It weighed 11 tons, had a 60 mm armour (maximum) and was armed with a single machine gun.

The small size and inadequate armament was recognised as a tactical limitation which was to some extent overcome by the Matilda II, or Infantry Tank Mk II. This vehicle had a 2 pdr gun, 78 mm armour thickness, well protected track and suspension and

The BT-7 (above) was one of several Soviet tanks developed from Christie's original fast tank design.
The Matilda II (below) was the most heavily armoured British tank in 1939.

weighed over 26 tons. It had a speed of 15 mph. Over 3,000 Matilda IIs were built and the type was in service from 1940 to 1943.

The 1930s saw many attempts to produce amphibious tanks and Vickers were one of the leaders in the field. There were several related designs based on the chassis and running gear of the Vickers light tank. It had a flotation hull and propellers driven by a power take-off from the engine. The British Army did not adopt this type of vehicle but the Russians did. Their T-37 of 1932 was a very close copy of the Vickers model, several of these having been purchased for trials and production rights acquired.

In 1934 Vickers Armstrong designed a new medium tank, the A9, to meet general staff requirements arising from the various 'Mechanised Force' experiments in the late 1920s. Thus the cruiser tank came into being. It was virtually the old medium tank under another name, the new designation being more descriptive of its function. The A9 was lighter than the abortive 16 tonner which had never gone into

production – it could use a standard bus engine and was built to simpler engineering standards, thus saving money. The 3 pounder gun which had been used in the Vickers medium tanks was supplanted by a new 2 pdr gun of higher velocity.

A close support version of the vehicle was also developed in which the 2pdr was replaced by a 3.7 inch howitzer. The function of the close support tanks was to fire smoke shells to cover a withdrawal or attack. The A9 was

approved for production in 1936, as the Cruiser tank Mk I. About 150 were built and were in service with the British Army at the outbreak of the Second World War. Interesting features were the retention of twin auxiliary machine gun turrets on the hull front, which had been an original feature of the 16 tonner of 1930. A simple but effective 'slow motion' suspension was incorporated which was retained in some subsequent designs. The A9 was 19 ft long, weighed

The American M26 Pershing was the heavy tank which was rushed into service in early 1945 to supplement the existing medium tank, the Sherman. Main armament was a 90 mm gun. Some were supplied to Britain.

Suspension was by torsion bars.
Opposite, top: A late model of the Churchill AVRE, based on the Churchill VII. This was the last model of the Churchill in service, surviving until 1965.

Right: The Japanese Kyu-Go Type 95 light tank was typical of the small Japanese tanks of the Second World War. This one is a museum exhibit at the RAC Centre at Bovington.

just over 14 tons and had a crew of six. The maximum armour thickness was 14 mm, and the hull was boat-shaped to reduce blast damage from mine explosions.

In Russia the Five Year Plans were put into effect to set the country on an industrial footing, and tank production on a really big scale started 1932.

A key vehicle at this time was the British Vickers 6 ton tank, of which 15 were purchased in 1931. The simple but reliable design was liked and a Russian-built version, the T-26, was put into production. This became the most important Russian tank type of the next few years and was the key armoured vehicle in infantry tank regiments. The T-26A, the earliest version, had twin gun turrets, while the T-26B had a single turret and 45 mm gun. There were many special variants including flame-throwers, command tanks, and even a bridge carrier. T-26 variants remained in service in some numbers up to 1942 and even later.

The standard Russian medium and heavy tanks were the T-28 and the T-35 both inspired by British designs, the 16 tonner and 'Independent' respectively. The T-28 was developed in 1932 and had as main armament a 76.2 mm gun, with two auxiliary machine gun turrets. There were several variants, including a command tank with frame aerial. The T-28 was 24 ft 9 in long, 9 ft 4 in high and wide, and its maximum armour thickness was 30 mm. It was quite a fast vehicle for its size (25 mph) but by 1939 it was considerably outmoded, being a bulky target and too thinly armoured. Many vehicles were rebuilt in 1940 with added armour and an outer armoured sheath to the turret; this brought the maximum armour thickness to 80 mm. However, the vehicle was to be no match for the modern German tanks which it faced in the invasion of May 1941.

The T-35 was a 50 ton vehicle and only about 30 were built. It had a main turret with 76.2 mm gun and four auxiliary turrets, two with 37 mm guns, and two with machine guns (the 37 mm guns were later replaced with 45 mm guns).

The suspension was protected by 10 mm armour plates and a radio (with frame aerial) was a standard fitting.

The crew totalled ten men. Over 32 ft long and 11 ft 4 in wide, the massive T-35 was one of the biggest and most imposing tanks at the time of its introduction. Like the T-28, however, the T-35 was obsolescent by 1940 and fell easy prey to the invading German tanks in 1941.

In America, meanwhile, Christie continued his development work. Among his designs was the M1932, an enlarged version of the M1928 and M1931 vehicles which dispensed with a gun set in a turret and carried its gun in the front of a roomier hull.

In 1936 British Staff officers attended the Russian Autumn manoeuvres as official guests and observers and were astonished at the impressive performance put up by vast numbers of the Christie-type tanks, which in speed outclassed all existing British designs. It was decided that there was a strong case for a British 'fast cruiser' tank, and the Nuffield Group of motor manufacturers were asked by the War Office to acquire an agency from Walter Christie for production and development of his fast tank design. The M1932 prototype, rejected by the American forces, was accordingly purchased for £8,000 and shipped to Britain in November 1936.

Tests in 1937 showed that while the M1932 lived up to promise in performance and reliability it suffered from major limitations for service use. The main problem was the narrow hull, a shortcoming aggravated by the space taken up each side by the heavy suspension units which were sandwiched between the inner and outer hull walls. To take the 2 pdr gun and turret standard on the existing A9 cruiser tanks it was necessary to rebuild the vehicle completely, retaining suspension, and engine and transmission, but widening the hull. In the process the little-used road running facility was abandoned. The completed vehicle, officially designated in the A13 series, became known as Cruiser Tank Mk. III. The prototype A13E2 was first of a whole range of British cruiser tanks developed during the Second World War, all with Christie suspension. Production of A13 started in 1939, only two years after it was conceived, and these tanks were widely used in France in 1940 and in the Western Desert in 1940–41. The A13 was a fast and powerful machine, and

more reliable than most of its successors into the bargain.

A tank that was virtually the equivalent of Vickers 6 ton tank was the Czechoslovak LTM-35, which appeared in 1934. This was similar in layout to the Vickers 6 tonner, but had rear wheel drive. The vehicle weighed 10·5 tons and had a 37 mm gun, and 35 mm maximum armour. The suspension system was very efficient, and with a 12-speed gearbox and servo-mechanical steering this vehicle was particularly easy to drive. The LTM-35 became the standard Czech Army tank and was exported to several countries including Sweden, Switzerland and Rumania. The builders were Skoda. The other major Czech type was the TNBH or LT-34, produced by CKD principally as a commercial venture for export, although from 1938 it was also ordered for the Czech Army. The TNPH was an 8 tonner with a 37 mm gun and a layout very similar to the Vickers 6 tonner. The vehicle had large road wheels on stub axles and leaf springs. It was a simple but rugged design which was very easy to maintain. The vehicle was under 15 ft long, its maximum armour thickness was 25 mm and its top speed was 36 mph (or 25 mph in later models). There were nine models altogether. Versions of the TNPH were supplied to Sweden, Yugoslavia, Afghanistan, Peru, Switzerland and Latvia. It was evaluated but not purchased by the British.

Italy's first tank dated from 1918 when it was proposed to make a licence-built version of the French Renault FT light tank. However, there were many delays and the Italian model, the Fiat 2000, did not enter service until the early 1920s. In 1929 the Italian Army purchased some Carden-Loyd tankettes and this design became the basis for a series of Italian light tanks of similar size and layout. These vehicles, which included bridgelayers and flame-thrower variants, proved quite satisfactory in the Italian colonies, and in the invasion of Abyssinia in 1935 against negligible opposition they were used to great effect. Some Italian tankettes took part in the Spanish Civil War where they encountered Russian made tanks which soon show-up the total inadequacy of the tankette type of vehicle. As a result a new

Top: the Russian T-37 amphibious light tank of 1932 had balsa filled floats and horizontal scissors suspension units.
Below: the T-26 was a Russian development of the Vickers 6 ton tank. This is a commander's vehicle, with radio antenna round the turret.

heavier type of light tanks was designed, the L/6 which weighed nearly 7 tons and had a turret with 20 mm gun. This vehicle was yet again clearly inspired by the Vickers 6 tonner, which it resembled quite closely in size and layout. The L/6 remained in service until 1943 when Italy surrendered.

As a result of Spanish Civil War experience it was also decided to make a 'tank destroyer' and concurrently with L/6 development, designs and prototypes were put in hand for both the tank destroyer and 'breakthrough' tank. The resulting prototype was turretless, having a fixed superstructure with gun and machine guns in the front apertures. This was considered an unsatisfactory arrangement so a second design was put in hand which had a lower superstructure carrying the main 37 mm gun, and a turret with machine guns. The new vehicle was designated M11/39. Only 70 of these were built,

due mainly to the limitations imposed by having the big gun in the hull. The revised design, the M13/40, had a 47 mm gun in the turret, and two machine guns in the nose. This type became the best known of all Italian tanks. It had a V-8 diesel engine, 25 mm armour, was of all-riveted construction, and had a top road speed of 20 mph, or half that cross-country. Total production was about 2,000 vehicles, including improved variants.

Like the Italians, the Japanese had an undistinguished record in AFV development, especially in the inter-war years. Their designs were usually highly derivative though a few ingenious ideas were exhibited. In the early days all Japanese tanks were purchased abroad and features from foreign designs, notably British, were later incorporated into Japanese made products. In 1918–19 Japan purchased a few British tanks and in the following years more types were acquired,

mainly British and French. The first full production type in Japan was the Type 92 tankette which appeared in 1932. This was based on the Carden-Loyd tankette and light tank produced in Britain. It had a simple spring and bell crank suspension and its thin armour could be penetrated by rifle fire. It was 10 ft 3 in. long, 5 ft 3 in. wide and 5 ft 4 in. high. The Type 92 was soon obsolete but nevertheless it was in service until about 1943, in its later years being used to tow tracked supply trailers to support the infantry.

By 1935 a new enlarged design had been developed, the Type 95 Kyu-Go. This was in production from 1939 until 1943, over 1,000 being built. This vehicle was 14 ft 4½ in. long and 7 ft 2 in. high. Its main weapon was a 37 mm calibre gun and there were two 7·7 mm machine guns, one in the turret rear. This tank had some neat features but in the Second World War it proved no match for the British tanks and anti-tank guns. The Japanese had limited opportunities for deploying tanks and they were more often than not used singly or in pairs to support the infantry advances along jungle paths. The Kyo-Go weighed 16,800 pounds. Its 12 mm armour plate was of rivetted construction.

Other Japanese acquisitions from abroad were Vickers Medium tanks and French Renault NC-1 tanks. These were virtually enlarged versions of the old Renault FT and were purchased in 1927. Modified in Japan the type was called the Etsu-B. This had a speed of 15 mph and was 14½ ft long. The Vickers design was closely copied in layout to produce the Type 89 and its similar successor the Type 92. These vehicles had a 57 mm gun, were 17½ ft long and weighed 13/15 tons. Both types were used extensively in the fighting against China in the 1930s and proved rugged and effective. They were still in use at the start of the Second World War The best Japanese tank was the Type 97 Medium, in use 1939-45.

A major development in military vehicles between the wars was that peculiar hybrid with wheels at the front and tracks at the back known as the half-track. The idea was first tried by Adolphe Kegresse, who had managed the Czar of Russia's personal transport fleet before the Revolution of 1917. In 1910, Kegresse had perfected a track to replace the rear wheels of cars to give better traction in snow and after he fled from Russia in 1918, he took his idea to the motor manufacturer André Citroen, who was impressed. In essence the Kegresse track was a rubber band round two guide wheels, with a sprung multi-wheel bogie attached to the leading guide wheel to provide a good length of ground contact for the track. The guide wheels were attached via a frame to the vehicle's rear axle.

The half-track greatly improved the road-holding of a vehicle and gave it excellent traction over quite rough ground, and it clearly had valuable military applications. Both France and Britain acquired military versions of Citroen half-track touring cars, and one or two of the rival half-track systems which also appeared. Of these the Roadless was best known, a British system produced by a team of demobilised tank designers who had set up in business to build equipment for commercial use.

Citroen produced a military gun tractor based on the half-track tourer chassis in 1928 and the type was sold in some numbers to the French and American Armies. The gun crew rode on the vehicle while the gun was towed behind – an excellent concept of mobility which completely usurped the old idea of horse drawn artillery. It took only a little imagination to realise that an armoured version had its uses – a sort of half-track armoured car. This gave rise to the French Autochenille series which saw service from 1929 onwards. The definitive production vehicle, the Autochenille 29 had a

37 mm gun and a machine gun in a traversing turret, and 12mm of armour. It could travel at 28 mph and had a front roller device as an aid to climbing out of ditches. Large numbers of these Autochenilles served with French 'mechanised cavalry' units and in 1940 were still in wide service.

The U.S. Army had produced its own design of half-track by 1935. This was derived directly from Citroens, but using American components. By 1938 a definitive design open-topped and with flat sides, was in production. In fact this married the body work of a White armoured car with a half-track chassis. The M2 half-track, as it was designated, served as a personnel carrier initially for mechanised cavalry units, but by 1940 was used by the infantry and artillery as well. During the Second World War, half-tracks saw universal use, with many variations from the original basic design.

In Germany as the Wehrmacht re-armed in the 1930s, the half-track type of vehicle was most thoroughly developed, on a scale which surpassed that of the other major armies. In the early years of the decade plans existed on paper for the expansion and mechanisation of the small standing army

Italian tanks before the Second World War were generally ineffectual. The L/6 (top), which entered service in 1940, had a turret-mounted 20 mm gun, while the contemporary M11/39 had a 37 mm gun mounted in the hull and a machine gun in the turret. Few of these tanks were built.

and from 1933 when Hitler became Chancellor, re-armament started in earnest, limited only by Germany's other industrial requirements.

The infantry and artillery elements of the German armoured divisions were to be fully motorised so that they could accompany the tanks, and a family of standard half-track types was evolved ranging from a small ½ ton half-track motor-cycle – the famous NSU Kettenkrad – up to an 18 ton vehicle which could be used in tank recovery and engineering roles. The other classes were 1 ton, 3 ton, 5 ton, 8 ton and 12 ton vehicles.

Compared with French and American half-tracks, the German designs were highly sophisticated. While the former had simple rubber tracks and elemental bogies, the German designs had interleaved bogie wheels with torsion bar suspension, manganese steel tracks as used on tanks, and a Cletrac steering brake which

The Tankette Type 92 (or Model 2592) was a Japanese vehicle similar to British light tanks. Designed in 1932, it was still in service in the Second World War.

acted within the transmission to assist steering by braking the track units. Drive was to the leading sprocket of the track unit which, in effect, took the place of the rear wheels in a conventionally driven truck. Open bodywork with seats was the general style adopted by the Germans, and Hanomag, Kraus-Maffei, and Henschel were the main builders of the various classes. These vehicles were used as gun tractors and by engineer units.

Armoured versions of the 1 ton (Sd Kfz 25D) and 3 ton Sd Kfz 251 vehicles became two of the best-known of all German military vehicles. In the Second World War half-tracks were converted and developed for many more fighting roles. The armoured models carried an armoured division's infantry, now classified 'panzergrenadiers' (armoured infantry).

As the spearhead of the German armoured divisions, a whole new family of tanks was designed and built. Some prototype tank vehicles were built in secret in the late 1920s,

German engineers having kept abreast of technological ideas by liaison with Sweden and Russia. The prototypes, Leichtetraktor and Grosstraktor (little and big tractors) were officially classed as agricultural vehicles but they had guns and turrets and were similar to contemporary foreign designs. Due to the severe German economic conditions of 1929–30, no further developments took place until 1932–34 when a full-scale re-armament programme started under Hitler's Third Reich regime. Four basic tank types were evolved, PzKpfw I, II, III and IV (PzKpfw – PanzerKampfwagen = armoured fighting vehicle). The PzKpfw I and II were light tanks which were put into priority production, mainly to equip the new panzer divisions very quickly with inexpensive vehicles available in large numbers. It was planned to replace these (except in reconnaissance units) with the much larger PzKpfw III and IV by 1939, but in the event progress lagged a little and the light tanks played a more prominent role in the Second World War than had originally been envisaged.

The PzKpfw I was actually based on the British Carden-Loyd light tank design. Krupp made the 5 ton defin-

itive production model, PzKpfw IA, starting in 1934. Later an improved version with longer chassis was built, the Model (Ausf) B, and there was a commander's model with fixed barbette instead of turret.

The PzKpfw II was built by MAN in its production form, a 10 ton vehicle with 6.2 litre engine and large leaf-sprung road wheels. While the PzKpfw I had machine gun armament, the PzKpfw II had a 2 cm gun. It was 15ft long. Nearly 1,000 PzKpfw IIs were in service in 1939.

Main armament of the panzer divisions was scheduled to be the PzKpfw III, a 15 tonner with 3.7 cm gun in its original form. The prototypes appeared in 1936 and a Daimler-Benz design was adopted. The early models were built in small numbers only, to try out various forms of suspension and layout. As a result the first main production type, the PzKpfw III Ausf E did not appear until 1939 and the panzer divisions at the start of the Second World War were embarrassingly short of what was intended to be their main vehicle. The early PzKpfw III was $18\frac{1}{2}$ ft long, had a maximum armour thickness of 14 mm and a speed of 20 mph.

Last of the four main German types of the 1930s was the 20 ton PzKpfw IV which was intended as a support tank to equip some platoons in each battalion. The definitive design built from 1937 was by Krupp, though other makers had also produced prototypes. The PzKpfw IV had small road wheels on leaf springs, a 3.7 cm gun and 30 mm armour. It had a top speed of 25 mph. In the event, the PzKpfw IV was to become the main German tank of the Second World War, eclipsing the smaller tanks it was designed to supplement. Both the PzKpfw III and IV were also built as command and observation tank variants, and later in the war they formed the basis for dozens of special purpose versions.

When Germany annexed Czechoslovakia in 1939 all the Czech tanks were impounded and production of the TNPH was continued for German use. In German service the LTM-35 was designated PzKpfw 35 (t) – 't' for Czechoslovakia. In 1940 these Czech vehicles formed a large proportion – some 25 per cent – of German tank strength, and the PzKpfw 38(t) was standardised as a German vehicle, being subsequently adopted for many major roles. The Czech arms industry became quite significant in the 1930s; these two major tank types were numerically most important, particularly after Germany took control.

The Czech tanks allowed the panzer divisions to build up to full strength in 1939, and by that time Germany had the most powerful and best equipped army in the world. The effectiveness of the tank and armoured division tactics, foreshadowed in small ways by Italy's invasion of Abyssinia in 1933 and in the Spanish Civil War in 1937, was demonstrated on a grand scale on September 1, 1939, when the German conquest of Poland started. The 'blitzkrieg' strategy which achieved the swift crushing of Poland was spearheaded by armoured divisions backed by supporting aircraft. The mobile concept of war had come of age and the Second World War was to take its development onwards dramatically.

Top: the two principal Japanese tanks of the 1930s, Types 92 and 93.
Centre: an SdKfz 251 platoon command half track, mounting a Pak 37 gun.
Bottom: the classic Czech TNHP, in Germany Army service as a PzKpfw 38 (t).

THE AFU WAR

The outbreak of war in September 1939 found both of Germany's western opponents, Britain and France, militarily unprepared. In France, at least, there was a delusion of security, for the early 1930s had seen completion of the immensely well fortified Maginot Line along the entire Franco-German border. This network of fortifications was considered impregnable and the politicians claimed that in the event of war with the traditional enemy Germany, Frenchmen could sit safely at home immune from attack. As was to be proved only a few months later,

The Hotchkiss H35 was typical of the French cavalry tanks, and formed the backbone of the armoured divisions in the Spring of 1940 when these two were pictured on patrol.

this was a fallacy for it took no account of air attack or the possibility of attack from another direction.

In the years before the war, however, these delusions were used as an excuse for intransigence in military thinking. In material terms the French Army was on paper one of the best equipped in the world, with over 3,500 tanks available in May 1940 compared with only about 2,600 in German hands. However the organisation of French armoured forces was piecemeal, mainly based on the infantry support role envisaged in the First World War. In fact, tanks were considered a mobile form of artillery and the new French tanks built in the 1930s were mainly heavily gunned and well armoured at the expense of speed. The

exceptions were the cavalry tanks, light low vehicles which were used to mechanise the old cavalry regiments.

The Hotchkiss H35 and H37, Renault R35, R37, and R39, were examples of cavalry tanks, all with two-man crews, $1\frac{1}{2}$ inch armour and 37 mm guns. With top speeds of 20–25 mph these were the fastest French tanks. Smaller still was the Renault AMR, with a 13 mm machine gun and weighing 5 tons, roughly equivalent to the British and German light tanks. In the medium category was the diesel-engined FCM 36, very well armoured but too slow to take advantage of its excellent shape and quality. It was one of the earliest tanks with all-welded construction.

The larger French tanks were really

very little advanced from the vehicles of the First World War. The Char D-1 and D-2 were 22 tonners with plain rhomboid shape and a turret-mounted 47 mm gun; their top speed was 14 mph. The Char B and its later development the B-bis were even closer to First World War ideas. They had thick armour, $2\frac{1}{4}$ inch maximum, nose-mounted 47 mm guns, and turret-mounted 37 mm guns. Weight was 34–36 tons and top speed 18 mph. The design was ideal for attacking trench systems of the type found on the Western Front in 1917–1918.

In the event the Char B also influenced the earliest British ideas for tanks in the Second World War. Various conflicting design agencies worked on tanks, and Tritton, Swinton, and other early pioneers were called in to produce a tank suitable for

expected trench warfare conditions on the Western Front. They designed a vehicle not unlike the Char B, but also with many characteristics of First World War designs, including sponsons. An immense 50 tonner it was soon named 'TOG', a whimsical allusion to 'The Old Gang'. Several variants were proposed but the project was overtaken by events within six months when the German lightning invasion of France and Flanders showed that the days of trench warfare were past.

The Royal Ordnance Factory was also given the task of building a 'shelled area' – or trench warfare – tank. This was the A20, again very similar to First World War designs. The hastily made prototype proved a failure but it formed the basis of the A22, later the Churchill, a heavy infantry tank which

nonetheless retained the A20 shape. In its early form the Churchill Mk I retained a hull-mounted 3-inch howitzer inspired by the Char B. The A22 design was hastily conceived and produced, and although production started in 1941 it was dogged by teething troubles, some of which were not overcome for another year or so.

Thus the Churchill took no part in the early tank actions of the war. Such tank fighting as there was in France after the German attack of May 1940 involved the pre-war types which equipped Britain's sole armoured division and her few tank brigades.

The predominant British service

Light tank Mk.IV was one of the light tank series developed by Britain in the late 1930s, and this one was still in use for energetic training in 1940. It had a top speed of 36 mph from a Meadows six-cylinder engine.

Cruiser Tank Mk.IV was one of the British designs derived from Christie's original prototypes. It weighed 14¾ tons and had a Liberty engine giving a top speed of 30 mph. Gun was a 2 pdr.

types were light tanks, cheap to produce in the financially stringent 1930s, and ideal for colonial work – there were over 1,000 in service in 1939. By 1940 the latest type was the Light Tank Mk VI, actually only suitable for reconnaissance but in fact forming a major part of the total tank strength. The infantry tank just entering service was the Matilda, Infantry Tank Mk II, successor to the Infantry Tank Mk I with the same name. The Matilda II was, in qualitative terms, an excellent tank for its day, and Matildas proved more than a match for the German tanks in an engagement at Arras, the only real Anglo-German tank-versus-tank action prior to the British withdrawal at Dunkirk in May 1940. In the early part of the war in the Western Desert the Matilda II was very successful, immune to all Italian tanks and anti-tank guns. It was no match, however, for the German tanks and heavy anti-tank guns when they arrived in 1941. There were several marks of Matilda, all varying in engines and minor details. The A13 Cruiser Tank Mk III was in service by mid-1939 and was used in France in 1940 and in the Western Desert campaigns of 1940–41. A subsequent development was the

Cruiser Tank Mk IV (A13 Mk II) which was simply the original A13 with additional armour plating which brought the armour thickness up to 30 mm. Extra plates were added to the turret side to give faceted faces which altered the vehicle's appearance a little. The original turret shape was retained beneath the faceted armour and the effect was of so-called 'spaced armour', a technique later used extensively by the Germans. The additional armour exploded shells on contact, leaving the main armour beneath it untouched.

From the A13 Mks I and II it was a short step to a much more sophisticated design, the A13 Mk III, better known as the Covenanter. By the time this vehicle was designed in early 1939 war was clearly imminent, and an urgent re-armament programme was in progress. The Covenanter, also known as the Cruiser Tank Mk V, was actually designed by the London Midland and Scottish Railway Company, to use their heavy engineering facilities which were earmarked for munitions work in wartime. As many existing A13 parts as possible were used but 30 mm armour thickness was built into the design from the start. It was also desired to keep the height of the vehicle as low as possible and to this end the old fashioned Liberty engine was replaced by a specially designed Meadows flat-12 motor. To save more space, the radiator and cooling system

was moved to the front, alongside the driver. The first Covenanters were ready in 1940, but the design proved to be a technical failure. Severe cooling problems were experienced and were never fully remedied despite extensive design modifications. As a result the very promising Covenanter was relegated to a training role and was never used in battle.

The replacement for the Covenanter was the Cruiser Tank Mk VI (A15), better known as the Crusader. This became the most important British cruiser tank and one of the most famous tanks of the war, particularly for its exploits in the Western desert where it became the main tank of the armoured divisions in 1941–42. The design represented a logical development from the original A13, and many A13 parts were used. The vehicle was longer and higher and the original Liberty engine was retained. The pilot model was ready by early 1940 and orders for over 1,000 vehicles were placed. Eventually nine factories were involved in building Crusaders and 5,300 were completed by 1943 when production ceased.

Due to the speed at which it was developed the Crusader suffered from several major mechanical defects, and it was not always reliable in service. But it was much respected by the Germans for its speed and was at its best during the desert fighting in 1942.

In Russia, new developments also stemmed from the BT series and led to the development of the T-34, one of the best known and most extensively produced tanks of all time. At the time of its appearance in battle, in 1941, the T-34 represented a concept so advanced that it rendered all then existing German tanks virtually obsolete. By implication, it similarly overshadowed all contemporary British and American designs of the time, although, of course, it was not matched in combat against tanks from these countries.

The significant features of the T-34 design were its slope-sided superstructure, its wide tracks with low ground pressure, its high speed, and its relatively high velocity heavy gun (originally 76 mm), which was more powerful than any other in contemporary German service.

The process of evolution from the BT to the T-34 was simple and direct. The first stage was a modernised version of the BT-7 tank, the BT-7M, which appeared in 1936. By this time, of course, the basic BT design was capable of improvement and in the BT-7M this was effected by replacing the original adapted aero engine with a V-12 four-stroke diesel engine which was developed specifically for tank

Above: Crusader III with 6 pdr gun was a late model in the series. Earlier vehicles had the 2 pdr. Christie suspension and turret shape reveal its development from the Cruiser Mk.IV (page 55).
Right: the Soviet line of development from the same Christie prototypes culminated in the classic T-34, most advanced tank in the world when it appeared in 1941, with a powerful 76 mm gun. This one is engaging a German tank at point blank range.

use in the 1930s. Increased range, reduced maintenance needs, and better cold-weather performance were the operational benefits derived from this motor, the V-2. Hull shape and hence shot-deflection in the BT-7M was improved by replacing the boat-shaped BT hull front by a slightly angled sloping nose (or glacis) plate. A hull machine gun was fitted and a 76.2 mm partly-stabilised gun was carried in the turret.

The next stage was an experimental tank, the BT-1S, which had sloping hull sides extended over the top of the tracks to the full width of the vehicle, and a slope-sided turret.

Experience with the BT-7M and BT-1S led to the building of a new vehicle based on the BT-7M chassis. This was the A-20 which had the new slope-sided hull shape but retained the old wheel or track running facilities of the BT series. It was seen, however, that there were design limitations in the A-20 which would prevent the fitting of a larger gun. An enlarged vehicle, the A-30, later called the T-32, was therefore designed which ran on tracks only, had armour up to 60 mm thick, and a 72.2 mm gun. In 1939 this prototype was successfully tested and, with modifications – mainly to the transmission – this vehicle was used as the basis for a new design, the T-34. The significant change, as in Britain, was the dropping of the original Christie idea of the ability to run on wheels or tracks. In practice this option was the dropping of the original act of removing then replacing the tracks was both tedious and time consuming. The T-34 ran on tracks only and a conventional lever and transmission brake system of steering replaced the steering wheel and pivoted front axles of the earlier Christie-based vehicles.

The first T-34s were ready in March 1940 and they were successfully tested in an arduous but trouble free trial run from Kharkov to Smolensk and back. Simplicity was the keynote of the T-34 design, and the finish was rough but serviceable. It lent itself to mass-production and maintenance was easy. The engine and transmission were at the rear with good accessibility. Because of the war situation in 1940 (at which time Russia had only been involved in the brief Russo-Finnish War) the T-34 was put into production with great rapidity, so quickly that many of the early models suffered numerous mechanical defects. A large tank arsenal for making T-34s was specifically built at Kirov.

The T-34's existence remained a close secret, however. When Germany invaded Russia in June 1941 the first Soviet tanks encountered were the lightly built (and by then obsolescent) vehicles of the 1930s. The Germans claimed to have destroyed or captured 20,000 of them in the opening months of the campaign, Operation Barbarossa.

While concentrating on the development of the T-34, the Russians did not neglect heavy tanks. To replace the T-35 and outfight any known foreign tank, two very large multi-turreted vehicles were produced in small numbers for test purposes. These were the T-100, a 56 tonner, and a similar but slightly smaller vehicle, the SMK. The armour had a maximum thickness of 60 mm, proof against contemporary 3.7 cm anti-tank and tank guns. These vehicles had a 76.2 mm gun in a barbette-mounted turret, and a 45 mm gun in a lower forward turret. Wide tracks and torsion bar suspension gave them a good performance for their huge size.

The few T-100 and SMK tanks which were available were sent for combat tests to the Finnish front early in 1940 where they proved very vulnerable, due to their large size and limited mobility. No further vehicles of this sort were built.

In addition to the twin turreted T-100 and SMK, the Russians de-

signed a single-turret model which was a shortened version of the larger vehicles with only the main turret installed. The chassis was proportionately shorter but the engine was the same 400 bhp petrol unit. With considerably less hull weight, armoured side skirts were originally contemplated but this idea was dropped before the prototype was built in September 1939.

Instead the hull and turret armour was thickened in places. A few trial vehicles saw combat in the Russo-Finnish War of winter 1939-40 and proved successful, being virtually immune to Finnish anti-tank guns. The maximum armour thickness on the hull was 75 mm and the turret front was even thicker. The new vehicle was designated KV (later KV-1), short for Klimenti Voroshilov, the famous Russian military leader. Production vehicles appeared in 1940 and the type soon replaced earlier heavy tanks. It was a very advanced design by contemporary standards, much bigger, for instance, than Britain's Matilda tank of the same period. Like the T-34, the KV was simple in construction and crude

in finish, lending itself well to mass production. It was all-welded (at a time when British and American tanks were still all-riveted), and production vehicles were powered by a 500 bhp V-12 diesel engine as in the T-34. There were several KV production models: KV-1A had a more powerful gun; KV-1B had extra bolted-on armour plates; KV-1C had a cast turret and 90 mm armour maximum; KV-1S was a lightened vehicle (60 mm armour, with the weight cut from 47 to 42 tons to give a corresponding increase in top speed).

The Russians were also quick to adopt the successful German idea of assault guns and tank destroyers to supplement and work with the tanks. A few experimental vehicles of this type had been built in Russia between the wars but with no specific tactical aims in view. The Germans developed assault guns or tank destroyers in 1939–40 on the PzKpfw III tank chassis. These were known as the Sturmgeschütze III, were cheaper and easier to produce than tanks, shared common maintenance and mechanical services, had a lower silhouette and

mounted a larger calibre gun (7.5 cm) than the PzKpfw III tank. The gun had only limited traverse because it was fitted to the hull in a fixed fighting compartment. Also in 1940 the Germans fitted guns in open-topped superstructures on obsolescent PzKpfw I tank chassis to produce Panzerjäger (tank destroyers) or Sturmhaubitze (assault howitzers), depending on the type of gun fitted.

The SU-76 was a Russian copy of the same idea. It utilised the lengthened chassis of the small T-70 light tank and had a 76 mm gun in an open-topped superstructure. The armour maximum was 25 mm. The SU-76 entered service early in 1943.

The Germans went on to produce a vast range of tank destroyer types and assault guns, all made by converting standard tank chassis, mainly older models. Most numerous and important were the Sturmgeschütze IV, similar to the StuG III but on a PzKpfwr IV

This cutaway museum exhibit of a German StuG III shows how the assault gun type of vehicle differed from a tank. Gun was mounted in hull instead of in the turret, allowing a larger calibre weapon and lower overall height.

chassis, the Panzerjäger IV which was lower and better armoured, and the Marder (tank destroyer) and Hornisse (assault gun) on the PzKpfw III and ex-Czech chassis.

With the SU-85 and the SU-100 the Russians outdid the Germans at their own game. Instead of using old chassis, the Russians based their tank destroyers on the T-34 tank chassis. The SU-85 appeared late in 1943, its high velocity gun being an adaptation of the 85 mm AA gun. The SU-100 was a further improved model with a 100 mm gun. One of the fastest and most heavily gunned tank destroyers to be used in the war, it remained in Russian service until the late 1950s and with Soviet satellite nations for many years beyond that. The SU-100 had a range of over 20,000 yards with high explosive shell and it could also fire armour piercing rounds, quite a considerable performance even by 1970 standards.

The Russians did not neglect to

The excellent T-60 light tank was a modern design which in 1940–41 complemented the Soviet T-34 medium tank. It was mainly used for reconnaissance, although the Russians used few light tanks in the latter part of the war.

improve their old pre-war designs as well. The T-60, for example, was a design intended to replace the various small pre-war light tanks. Unlike the previous light tanks, it was not amphibious, but it had a 20 mm aircraft type cannon, and the turret was offset to the left to allow the engine to be set on the right. The T-60 was the mainstay of the Russian armoured reconnaissance regiments. It had an excellent performance in snow, like all Russian tanks, and proved very successful. It was a very small vehicle, only 13 ft long and $5\frac{3}{4}$ ft high. The final development of the old T-26 series also served well into the Second World War. This was the T-26S, a greatly improved model which had a new turret, welded armour, radio, and some mechanical improvements. The T-26S saw quite wide service and there were also flame thrower and special purpose variants. The design was really obsolete, however, and T-26 production ceased as soon as the T-34 was readily available.

Apart from the Russian Front the other major theatre involving tank warfare on a large scale in 1941-42 was the Western Desert. The battle for

possession of North Africa and the route through Egypt to the Middle East was unique in that it took place in a region which was sparsely populated, was generally flat except for a few major physical features which influenced directions of movement, and was subject to extremes of climatic conditions. Tank fighting was in the open, concealment was difficult, and so speed became an important factor. Equally important was gun range and firepower, and in these respects the German Afrika Korps was superior.

The main German tanks in 1941, the PzKpfw III and IV, had 5 cm and 7.5 cm guns respectively. The latter was a low velocity weapon which fired high explosive shells, but it could greatly outrange all British tanks. The standard British tank gun was still the 2 pdr, in the Crusader, Matilda and Valentine tanks which equipped the British armoured regiments. Rommel, the German commander, was an infantryman turned tank general, whose division had spearheaded the German advance through Belgium into France in May 1940. He was a brilliant tactician who kept his divisions con-

stantly moving to cover enormous distances quickly, and he used the element of surprise whenever possible. One of his innovations was to use the 8.8 cm Flak ('88') anti-aircraft gun as an anti-tank weapon. It proved literally devastating in this role and soon became legendary. The '88' could pick off a British tank while well outside the effective range of the tank's gun.

Another new weapon was the 5 cm Pak 38 anti-tank gun, a replacement for the earlier 3.7 cm gun. The Pak 38, in a low profile field mount, was also superior in range and penetrating power to any British tank or anti-tank gun then in service. In fact, the Afrika Korps was always short of these powerful 8.8 cm and 5 cm guns – as it was of tanks – but the relatively small amount of good equipment available was effectively used and for most of the period between April 1941 and August 1942 the Germans were on the offensive, tying down and forcing back numerically superior British and Commonwealth forces.

Prior to the German involvement in the desert fighting the sole opponents to the British had been the Italians, the colonial rulers of Libya. In the early period of the desert war, June 1940–March 1941, they had proved no match for the much smaller British forces which advanced from Egypt against them. Like the British the Italians still depended on small, dated machines to make up the bulk of their tank forces. The CV 3/33 tankette was predominant and the most modern tank was the M13/40.

The M13/40 was not an exceptional design, even by 1940 standards, and in the Western Desert in 1940–41 it was no match for the British tanks, especially the well armoured Matilda which was virtually immune to all Italian guns.

A far better Italian vehicle was the Semovente 75/18 assault gun which was introduced in 1941. It was built on the chassis of the M13/40, having a low superstructure and a 75 mm howitzer in a limited traverse mount as in the German assault guns. This was used in the assault gun role in the desert with considerable success. It was later used in Italy in 1943, then by the Germans in Italy and by the Italian army again in 1945–47.

The Semovente was the only really successful and useful Italian tracked AFV of the Second World War, although by late 1942 Italy was making attempts to catch up. Two potentially good designs were produced, one a well armoured medium tank, the P.47 which was similar in layout and size to the American Sherman, and the Saharienne, which was an almost exact copy of the British Crusader. However, these were not developed after the Italian armistice in September 1943.

When the German tanks arrived in the desert, the balance of power changed considerably. As has been mentioned, the 5 cm gun of the PzKpfw III and the 7.5 cm low velocity gun of the PzKpfw IV both outranged the British 2 pdr. Furthermore the 2 pdr could only fire armour piercing (AP) rounds – a relic of the pre-War tank-versus-tank theories – so could not provide fire support for general attacks (field artillery – which was towed – had to be deployed for this role, an awkward and inflexible arrangement). The German tanks could fire high explosive rounds (HE) as well as AP, so had a tactical advantage as well as a firepower advantage.

This forced the British into an urgent programme of fitting a 6 pdr gun into the cruiser and infantry tanks. It was late 1942 before the Crusader cruiser tanks were so fitted, and before an infantry tank with this armament, the Valentine III, was in service in the desert (the Valentine was an infantry tank development of the old heavy cruiser tanks, A9 and A10). The 4/17 Churchill tank (not used in the Western Desert, due mainly to its slow speed and limited suitability) was also fitted with a 6 pdr gun, in which form it became the Churchill III or IV. The 6 pdr gun had been designed as early as 1939 but considerable official vacillation delayed its production until it became really urgent late in 1941. A version of the 6 pdr was also built on a field carriage as an anti-tank gun. One incidental development in anti-tank gun employment in the desert was the portee, a specially adapted truck which carried rather than towed a wheeled anti-tank gun (either 2 pdr or 6 pdr). The gun could be unloaded when and where required to go into action, and in most versions it could be fired from the vehicle. This portee idea provided

a useful element of mobility to supplement the limitations of the tanks in the British armoured divisions.

The 6 pdr gun did not see service until the summer of 1942, shortly before the decisive Battle of Alamein. However, the weapons which did most to swing the balance of firepower in Britain's favour at Alamein were the American medium tanks which became available at this critical and decisive time.

By the latter half of the 1930s, tank development in America had begun to move on from the doldrums of the lean years between the wars. The 5 and 15 ton weight limits were eased when it became obvious that tanks of these weights could not carry sufficient armament and armour to make them tactically worthwhile. The major new design of 1938–39 was the M2 light tank series which derived from a design based on the Vickers 6 tonner (the T3 light tank). This had the Vickers type suspension but for subsequent designs the American Ordnance Department designed a much stronger suspension. This had self-contained bogie-units, very easy to replace entirely in the event of damage. The final version of the M2, the M2A4, was approved for production late in 1939 when the war in Europe had just begun. The American armed services were woefully short of modern equipment and the M2A4 was put into mass-production – at a tractor plant, for the small US Army Ordnance facility at Rock Island Arsenal was too small to build tanks in any quantity. The M2A4 light tank was the first mass-produced American tank, over 800 being built.

In late 1940 a further improved model with new turret and lengthened suspension appeared, the M3 and this was the first American tank supplied to Britain under Lend-Lease in 1941, and was also the first American tank used in combat, albeit in British hands. The M3, known as the Stuart or unofficially as the 'Honey', was a fine reliable vehicle with a 37 mm gun and

Opposite, top: first of the many American light tanks of the Second World War was the M2A4. It weighed 10½ tons, was 14½ ft long, and had 25 mm armour. This US Marines vehicle is in the Solomons in 1942. Bottom: the M3 Stuart was a direct development and these vehicles, in British service, are on patrol in the Western Desert in early 1942.

25 mm armour. Though classed as a light tank by the Americans it was more equal in firepower, speed and size to the pre-war British cruiser tanks which it largely replaced.

In 1942 when the automotive industry had become closely involved in tank production, a new light tank, the M5 was designed as a direct result of the Cadillac firm's 'outside' look at the M3 design. There was a shortage of aero engines – now needed for a greatly expanded aircraft industry – and Cadillac adapted two of their commercial automobile engines and provided the vehicle with Hydramatic automatic transmission. The Ordnance Department were sceptical at first but the prototype completed a lengthy trial run with no trouble at all, the design was standardised. The M5 (and a later version, the M5A1) became the standard American light tank for the rest of the war. It was also used by the British, Free French and other Allied armies. Subsequently Hydramatic transmission was used in many American tanks, while a variety of alternative commercial engines were adapted to meet the ever-increasing need for engines to meet vehicle output. This gave rise to the profusion of subvariants in American wartime tanks, the different designations usually in-

dicating different engine installations or minor structural variations. For instance the light tanks M3 and M3A3 were essentially similar vehicles but the M3A3 had a modified welded hull shape (while the M3 was riveted) and a different engine.

The urgent need for a new medium tank was fulfilled by building in 1938 what was virtually an enlarged version of the M2 light tank. This new vehicle, the M2 Medium, had almost identical suspension, track and layout. It was of

Above: the M5 light tank was the later development of the American light tank series, with Cadillac engine and improved hull shape. This one is in Germany in early 1945.
Below: the M3 medium tank made a timely arrival in the Western Desert in the summer of 1942, giving the British a tank to outshoot the German tanks. Sponson-mounted 75 mm gun is seen here, with 37 mm gun in turret. These are Grants – a version built specifically for Britain.
Above, right: the M4 Sherman tank replaced the M3 and was mass-produced in purpose built tank arsenals.

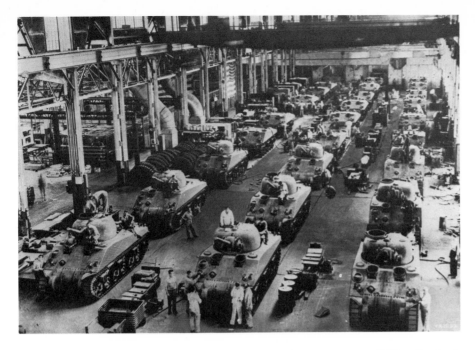

in 1939, and was followed a year later by a slightly improved model, the M2A1. By now America was only too aware of events in Europe and a mass rearmament programme was started to provide the US services with new modern equipment, for a war which, it seemed, would inevitably involve America sooner than later. US Ordnance Department specialists were quick to note the success of the German PzKpfw III and IV with their 5 cm and 7.5 cm guns and it was decided that a similarly armed American tank was urgently needed. The obvious candidate was a development of the M2/M2A1 mediums. However, the turret and turret ring of these vehicles were too small, so an interim arrangement was made, whereby a 75 mm gun was mounted in the hull front and the 37 mm gun and turret was retained. The idea for this came from an experimental self-propelled gun prototype of the M2 series, tried in 1939. With other modifications the new vehicle was designated Medium Tank M3 and was rushed into production early in 1941. The 75 mm gun was a development of the famous hard-hitting French '75' field gun of First World War fame, which the US Army had adopted in 1917.

riveted construction, had a 37 mm gun in a central turret, and machine guns in the superstructure to give an all-round field of fire. Deflection plates on the rear hull were arranged to ricochet bullets sideways, a vestigial remnant of the old trench warfare requirements of the First World War. The medium tank was still, of course, seen as an infantry support vehicle as tanks were at that time still an infantry responsibility in the US Army. In 1940, however, an Armored Force was formed,

and took over responsibility for both the Infantry's tanks and the Cavalry's combat cars.

The use of parts common with the light tank was a useful step in the direction of standardisation which was more fully exploited in the years ahead. To obviate the need for developing a powerful engine for the big (22 ton) vehicle, a de-rated Wright Continental aircraft engine (a 400 bhp air-cooled radial unit) was adapted for tank use.

The first M2 medium entered service

America now had a most effective,

albeit expedient, medium tank able to meet any other 1940–41 tank on equal terms of firepower. What was needed was quantity production and this was achieved quickly by harnessing the vast American automobile industry to the needs of war. In earlier years the US Ordnance Department had planned to use heavy engineering firms (like Baldwin and Alco) for AFV construction, but in 1940 it was seen that even these big firms could not build tanks fast enough. Chief of the military vehicle re-armament programme was William Knudsen, of General Motors, and he conceived a plan to use automobile manufacturers to turn out tanks in tens of thousands, using their flow-line techniques to achieve speed of production and quality of output. This meant building new factories in most cases, since automobile plants were not suitable for AFV production. In the 1941–42 period, therefore, vast new tank arsenals were built by the major motor-car builders, mainly in the Detroit and Michigan areas. They leased and operated the plants on behalf of the government at nominal rents. The US Ordnance Department set up an office in Detroit to co-ordinate design and development.

The first M3 medium tanks were coming off the line in April 1941 even while Chrysler's tank arsenal – the first one – was being built around it. This tank was later called the Lee while a special version with modified turret built to British requirements was called the Grant. In the early summer of 1942 the first 300 of these vehicles arrived in Egypt for British service and finally gave the British 8th Army a tank with a gun which could outshoot the German tanks. From then on British fortunes in the desert fighting began to recover.

Meanwhile in America work carried on to produce a medium tank which could carry the 75 mm gun in a traversing turret rather than in the limited traverse hull-mount of the M3. With a wider hull, bigger turret and bigger turret ring, the M4 medium tank appeared late in 1941 and was rushed into production to replace the M3 on the line. The M4, later called the General Sherman or just plain Sherman, became the key Allied tank of the Second World War. It thus rated with the Soviet T-34 as one of the most important AFV designs of all time (at one

time the Germans nicknamed the T-34 the 'Soviet-Sherman'). Over 42,000 Shermans or Sherman-based variants were built, and some armies, notably Israel's, were still using up-dated versions in 1970. In 1942 however, the Sherman was just coming into service and the first were sent (via the Lease-Lend scheme) to Egypt where they made a spectacular operational debut in British hands at the Battle of Alamein in October 1942.

An important new feature of the Sherman was its gyro-stablized gun mount, which made it possible to fire the gun accurately while the vehicle was on the move (previously, accurate aimed fire was possible only when a tank was stopped, and thus when it presented a better target to the enemy). The stabilizer henceforth became a standard fitting in most new tank designs, the Germans copying the idea in the Panther in 1944.

In the Western Desert fighting the armoured car had a new lease of life. Between the wars the light tank and tankette had begun to usurp the armoured car's patrol and reconnaissance role, and as a result relatively little development work was done before 1939. Indeed on the outbreak of war some nations (including Britain) were still using a few cars of First World War vintage – certainly in design if not actual date of construction. The Rolls-Royce of 1915 led directly to 1920 and 1924 machines which were only marginally different to the original design. They still gave excellent service in the desert war.

Many designs of the inter-war years were based on the then popular rigid six-wheeler commercial truck chassis. Crossley, Guy and Lanchester were typical British vehicles of this type (the latter on a specially built six-wheel chassis), and some were still in use in the early war period. Equivalent German designs were the Schwerer Panzershäfwagen (heavy armoured car) Sd Kfz 231, 232 and 263. They were well-proportioned vehicles but the cross-country performance of all these six-wheelers was limited as only their rear wheels were driven. By 1940 a new generation of armoured cars was appearing.

The Germans produced some fine rear-engined eight-wheel vehicles in which all the wheels drove and all

steered (there were duplicate controls for driving in either direction). These were low, tough and reliable machines with 14 mm armour. Models included the Sd Kfz 231 (with a 2 cm gun in turret), Sd Kfz 232 radio car (with 2 cm gun and prominent 'bedstead' aerial), the Sd Kfz 233 with 7.5 cm gun in an open limited-traverse mount, and the Sd Kfz 263 'Funkwagen', a radio-command car with roomy enclosed body. Experience in the Western Desert where these cars were widely used led to new improved vehicles, better protected mechanically for extremes of climate. The Sd Kfz 234 series had air-cooled Tatra diesel engines and models included the Puma (Sd Kfz 234/2), the Sd Kfz 234/4, and a wheeled tank destroyer which carried a 7.5 cm Pak 40 gun. These new types did not enter service until 1944, however, by which time the desert war was long forgotten and the need for armoured cars had diminished greatly.

Some light 4 × 4 armoured cars came out in 1936–37 and were even more widely used. The Sd Kfz 221, 222 and 223 were variously armed, had a 75 bhp Horch V-8 and 14 mm armour.

The Italians and French also made some fine armoured cars in the 1937–40 period, the Autoblinda 40 and the Panhard 178 being the best-known. These were four wheelers, the Panhard having a heavy gun and turret for its size and the Autoblinda having excellent mechanical refinement. It had free-running spare wheels arranged on the sides to give extra traction over rough ground and prevent bellying. Its shape and layout inspired some of the British four-wheel designs. It had a 20 mm gun and could run in either direction, having duplicate controls front and rear.

In 1938 Britain began work on a new generation of armoured cars. The Guy, based on the chassis of the Quad-Ant four-wheel-drive artillery tractor, had a hull and turret similar to contemporary light tanks – indeed it was originally called a 'wheeled tank'. The impetus for these new developments came from foreign designs and the

The invasion of Russia in June 1941 saw the Germans unleash a vast land assault, when the Panzer divisions swept aside all opposition in the early weeks of the campaign, using the well-tried 'blitzkreig' tactics perfected in Poland and France. Here a PzKpfw III moves forward to clear a street.

Guy armoured car which came into service early in 1940 and a Humber were not dissimilar in size or layout to the German Sd Kfz 223.

The Daimler company produced a new type of vehicle, the Scout Car, to a 1938 BSA design. Popularly but erroneously called the Dingo, this was a small open-topped vehicle originally intended for infantry reconnaissance but subsequently adopted as a 'runabout' by virtually all arms. It had all-wheel steering in its early form but this refinement was dropped to facilitate production. The Daimler Scout Car was of virtually 'monocoque' construction – the armoured body shell was the strength member with suspension and drive units attached.

A more advanced Daimler armoured car was derived from the Scout Car. This again dispensed with a chassis and had independent drive to all four wheels. It proved a highly successful vehicle which remained in service for many years after the war. A heavy armoured car was developed by AEC, based on the chassis of the well-known AEC Matador gun tractor. This 12 ton vehicle had a rear-mounted $7\frac{1}{2}$ litre diesel engine and in its later forms carried a 6 pdr or 75 mm gun, giving it the hitting power of contemporary British tanks. AECs were used widely in the desert fighting, where from 1941 armoured cars virtually replaced light tanks in British armoured divisions – in desert conditions armoured cars had all-round advantages and in particular were faster and more reliable.

This was not exactly the case in the US Army, however. Armoured car designs were produced in 1940 largely as a result of the study of foreign developments. The main American vehicles were the M8 (Greyhound) with 37 mm gun and a turretless scout car version of the same vehicle, the M20. The other major type was the Staghound which was built expressly for British requirements and resembled British vehicles in layout. Although the Staghound was intended for desert operations, the fighting in North Africa had ceased by the time it was available. Staghounds were used with success in later operations however. Another vehicle of interest in the 1943 period was the immense eight-wheel 23 ton Boarhound; this was almost as big as a Sherman tank, mounted a 6 pdr

Top: Humber armoured car was the main British armoured car in 1941–43. It weighed 7 tons, was 15 ft long, and had a 15 mm machine gun.
Centre: best British armoured car was the

Daimler, with 2 pdr gun, 16 mm armour, and 50 mph top speed. It entered service in 1941.
Above: Staghound was built in America by Chevrolet to British requirements. Its top speed was 55 mph.

gun and was expressly intended for desert operations. It appeared too late to see service and never entered production.

When the North African campaign ended in April 1943, the role of the armoured car became considerably less important. Tank development in Europe for the latter part of the war became an urgent matter for both the Allies and Germany, as each side sought to outgun and out-armour the other. The Russian T-34 gave impetus to this.

A heavy gun tank had been under development in Germany since 1937, but the requirements for this were continually shelved and altered. The vehicle was called a 'Durchbruchswagen' (DW or 'Break-through vehicle'). By 1941 the plans and specifications had been crystallised in the VK 3607 design, a 36 tonner with a 75 mm gun. When the T-34 was encountered, orders were given to develop the design with all despatch. It was modified to become the 45 ton VK 4501 which was larger to allow for much thicker armour (up to 110 mm) and a 8.8 cm gun modified from the standard high velocity Flak '88' AA gun. Henschel won the design competition from a Porsche petrol-electric design, (this was subsequently developed into a very heavy 'Panzerjäger' – tank hunter – the Elefant, also with a 8.8 cm gun but in a fixed superstructure).

The Henschel VK 4501 became the famous Tiger tank, the first vehicle being ready in April 1942 and production vehicles going into action for the first time the following September. The Tiger or PzKpfw IV Ausf E was an immense feat of engineering. It had 100 mm thick hull armour, interleaved road wheels with torsion bar suspension, morticed and welded armour plate joins, and a huge turret.

The early models had an elaborate engine 'breathing' system and were waterproofed for submerged crossing of rivers. The weight – finally over 54 tons – was excessive for most bridges and was a major tactical limitation. The engine was sometimes unreliable, maintenance was complicated and there was a complex arrangement with the wheels and suspension whereby the tracks and wheel trains were adapted for travelling or battle. This

Top: a Tiger displays its wide tracks, heavy turret and 8·8 cm gun, in Tunisia in 1942.
Centre: the Panther (PzKpfw V) was the German answer to the Russian T-34, with sloped overhanging hull sides and high velocity 7·5 cm gun. This particular vehicle has been captured by Soviet troops.
Above: The formidable Jagdpanther ('Hunting Panther') was a tank destroyer version of the Panther with an 8·8 cm gun.

involved an extra two tracks for every vehicle. The Tiger was a formidable fighting machine – the most power-fully armed tank in service when new – but its slow speed and slow gun traverse meant that it could be successfully stalked and destroyed by smaller tanks working in twos or threes. The first Tigers knocked out by the British at the end of the operations in North Africa fell to well emplaced 6 pdr guns.

While the Tiger was something of a retrospective compromise, completed in an up-gunned form to meet the changing situation the other major German tank, the Panther, proved to have one of the most balanced com-binations of speed, weight, armour and firepower of all Second World War designs.

The Panther (or PzKpfw V) was Germany's direct answer to the threat of the Soviet T-34, which had first been encountered in really large numbers in October 1941, when an entire German panzer division was severely mauled. This resulted in the urgent appoint-ment of a commission of officers, manufacturers and designers to ex-pedite the production of a German tank to beat the T-34. Early in 1942 designs were ready, one by Daimler Benz and another by MAN. The Daimler Benz design was virtually a

Top: A German armoured division moving into action in Russia in the summer of 1941. Panzer-grenadiers in their Sd Kfz 251 halftrack (left) over-take PzKpfw II tanks as they pass a decimated Russian supply convoy.

Above: A panzer division headquarters company at a Russian farm. Visible here is a command tank (Panzerbefehls wagen III), nearest the camera, with half-tracks and field cars of the headquarters staff beyond.

direct copy of the T-34 with rear engine and rear drive, but with provision for driving from inside the turret. This vehicle did not lend itself to German engineering however, so the MAN design was chosen for production.

This had a rear engine, front drive, interleaved road wheels with torsion bar suspension, and sloped armour all round in similar style to the T-34. There was a roomy turret set well back and fitted with a 7.5 cm 2/70 high velocity gun. The maximum armour thickness was 120 mm and the Maybach 630 bhp engine gave a 28 mph top speed. The Panther weighed about 45 tons and was 29 ft long over the gun. Prototypes were tested in the middle of 1942 and production started late that year with top priority status – at one time even aircraft manufacture was cut back to make resources (and fuel) available for Panthers. Nearly 6,000 vehicles were subsequently built, including some recovery versions (Bergepanzer Panther), commander's vehicles and observation post vehicles.

In 1943 the Panther design was modified still more to produce a self-propelled tank destroyer – the Jagdpanther – with an 8.8 cm gun, low in the hull in a limited traverse mount. It proved to be a very potent weapon.

Top: an Afrika Korps PzKpfw II in the Western Desert, 1941. This 10 ton vehicle with 2 cm gun was mainly used in the reconnaissance role, and also formed the basis for conversion to several types of assault gun.

Above: Half-tracks were used extensively in the panzer divisions to transport the support arms. This Sd Kfz 250/3 is the command vehicle of an artillery regiment in 21 Panzer-Division, Afrika Korps.

About 230 were built and the design is now considered a 'classic' of its era.

Although the Germans made enormous efforts they were never able to regain the initiative in tank warfare, nor were they able to produce tanks in anything like sufficient quantities. Several interim measures were taken. PzKpfw IV production was phased out by late 1943 and the PzKpfw IV was greatly improved by the addition of the long 7.5 cm gun and skirt armour in Models F2 and H.

From 1943 until the end of the war, Germany frittered away valuable resources in a series of projects which aimed to produce AFVs heavier and more powerful than any others. The chief architects of this policy were Hitler himself and Dr Ferdinand Porsche, the automotive engineer. Hitler took a great personal interest in tanks, and it was his own directives which led to the early use of the 5 cm and 7.5 cm guns for AFVs. Hitler became obsessed with the notion that Germany should possess tanks more powerful than any likely to be developed by other nations, and he found a ready ally in Dr Porsche, who had already proposed a monster 185 ton vehicle. This Maus (Mouse), which was originally to be called Mammut (Mammoth), was the largest AFV actually built in the Second World War. Only the two prototypes were completed by late 1944 when the deteriorating war situation led to their abandonment. The Maus (never actually armed) was planned to have a 15 cm gun and a co-axial 7.5 cm gun. The engine was central and drive was gas-electric with a top speed of 12 mph. No bridge could support the mighty weight of the vehicle so it was fitted for deep submerged wading (to 24 ft) for river crossing.

Although the Maus did not see service, an enlarged version of the Tiger did. This was the Tiger II, also called the Koenigs-Tiger (King Tiger or Royal Tiger). Designs for this were drawn up late in 1942, around an 8.8 cm gun as the main armament. Porsche and Henschel tendered designs and Henschel's model was put into production, although some vehicles had a Porsche turret. The Tiger II was a 68 tonner with 185 mm of armour and a speed of up to 28 mph. By the end of 1943 it was in production and nearly 500 had been built by March 1945, when tank construction in Germany ran down.

An even more formidable weapon than the Tiger II was the Jagdtiger, a tank destroyer version of the Tiger II fitted with a 12.8 cm gun in a limited traverse mount. This 70 ton vehicle had an armour maximum of no less than 250 mm and was the heaviest AFV actually to see service in the Second World War. A further development of the Tiger II was in the offing when the war ended; this was the Lowe (Lion) or Tiger-Maus, a planned 70 ton vehicle which was to have had the 12.8 cm gun. A development of the Panther, the Panther II, was in prototype form in 1945 when the war ended.

While the obsession with large vehicles was at its height, the German Ordnance Department proposed an AFV rationalisation programme, to utilise standardised components and automotive parts. Chassis in the 5, 10, 25, 50, 75 and 100 ton classes were proposed in a so-called 'E' series. Of these only the E.100 had been started in 1945 and the huge prototype, semi-complete, was captured by the British at the end of the war. The 'E' series represented a sound scheme for providing a fine family of AFVs for the conditions of the late war period but development came too late.

The super-heavy tank policy was proved to be wrong for the German position in 1944–45. For although in theory the big German tanks were almost impregnable in a direct shooting match with other tanks, this notion took no account of other important factors. First of these was the sheer weight of numbers in the quantity of tanks available to the Allies, and secondly there was Allied air superiority on all fronts. Rocket-firing fighter bombers (such as the Typhoon, Thunderbolt, and Sturmovik) were constantly available to attack and destroy any German heavy tank which might hold up an advance. The sheer size of the vehicles proved their undoing, too, for they were slow, sometimes subject to mechanical trouble, and limited tactically by bridge and road restrictions.

On the Eastern Front, the Soviets countered the bigger German tanks realistically. One of the first measures was to up-gun the T-34, especially after the appearance of the Panther, when it was modernised to take a larger turret with an 85 mm gun developed from a high velocity AA weapon. Known as the T-34/85, this vehicle had better firepower than the Panther and was put quickly into production. After 1945 the T-34/85 was used to equip all Soviet 'satellite' armies and in 1972 many were still in service. Production of the T-34/85 continued until 1964 and over 12,000

The immense Maus prototype dwarfs its crew and attendant technicians when on test. It was 29 ft 8 in long, 12 ft high, and had armour 240 mm thick on the turret front.

were built out of a total of well over 40,000 T-34 vehicles of all types.

The KV heavy tanks were similarly updated. The KV-85 had the same turret and gun as the T-34/85 (which it actually preceded in production) while a modernisation of the KV design led to the famous 'Josef Stalin' series of tanks, the IS family. Late in 1943 the IS-1 design was approved; basically this was the old KV-85 with a modified hull shape, new diesel engine, new transmission, and better shaped turret and superstructure. The early IS-1 had an 85 mm gun but this was soon replaced by a new 100 mm gun. In late 1943 an even more powerful weapon was fitted, the 122 mm gun, developed from a corps artillery field piece. This vehicle came into wide service in 1944 and in that year further redesign of the hull superstructure led to the IS-2 which had a well sloped, faired glacis plate and hull side.

Corresponding to battle tanks were the tank destroyers, the ISU-122 and ISU-152. These had the IS (or modified KV) chassis but a fixed superstructure and limited traverse mount. The ISU-152 was really an assault gun, the 152 mm gun being a low velocity weapon with excellent range and able to fire AP or HE rounds.

The SU-152 weighed 50 tons, had 75 mm armour (maximum), and the gun had a 19,000 yard effective range. By contemporary Western standards this was an immense vehicle and with such effective vehicles the Russians quickly gained and maintained superiority over the German AFVs for the remainder of the war.

For the Americans and their Allies the major effort in tank production was the M4 Sherman series, which became the basis for the larger part of the tank strength. On the basic M3 or M4 medium chassis there were

The ISU-122 was a Russian assault gun based on the Stalin tank. Like other Soviet designs it was simple in shape, easy to mass produce, and very heavily armed and armoured. Here two ISU-122s move forward with accompanying infantry in lorries, a normal Russian tactic at this time since troop carriers were in short supply and priority was given to tank production.
Below: the M7 Priest was a self-propelled gun (or motor gun carriage) based on the M3 or M4 medium tank chassis. It had a 105 mm howitzer adapted from a field mount. It was used by the British, Americans, and Free French.

recovery vehicles, mine exploders, gun tractors, anti-aircraft vehicles, rocket firers, and guns.

The self-propelled guns ('gun motor carriages' in American terminology) were the most important group. The M7 105 mm howitzer motor carriage had early success in the desert war where they provided the first truly mobile support fire for the British 1st Armoured Division at Alamein. Called the Priest, this vehicle was essentially an open-topped M3 or M4 with a 105 mm field howitzer mounted less its wheels. Priests were widely used from 1942 onwards and some were still being used by NATO forces in the 1960s.

The M10 3 inch gun motor carriage was developed more directly from the M4. This was a purpose-built tank destroyer with special slope sided hull and open turret, which appeared late in 1942 (over 10,000 were eventually built). An up-gunned version of this type of vehicle was the M36 with a long barrel 90 mm gun developed from a contemporary AA gun. This vehicle was in service in late 1944, the

The M18 Hellcat tank destroyer had a 76 mm gun, weighed 20 tons, had only 12 mm armour, and was almost 22 ft long over gun. It had torsion bar suspension and an open-topped turret.

most heavily gunned Allied AFV at the time of its appearance.

Most notable of all American self-propelled guns was the M18 Hellcat, fastest tracked AFV of the war, which could manage 50 mph and, being only lightly armoured, was used in 'hit and run' tactics when stalking and attacking the big German Tigers and Panthers.

Another major vehicle was the M8 howitzer motor carriage which had a 75 mm howitzer and was built on the Light Tank M5 chassis. This equipped the support companies of American tank battalions prior to the appearance of a special version of the Sherman with 105 mm howitzer in 1944.

At divisional and corps level the heavy mobile artillery vehicle was the M12 155 mm gun motor carriage, essentially using an old First World War French gun removed from its field carriage and placed on the stripped down chassis of the M3 or M4 medium tank. Although regarded at first with some suspicion by artillerymen, the M12 proved to be a valuable weapon in North West Europe after the Allied invasion of June 1944. In 1945 the M12 was replaced by the M40, a similar vehicle with a modern 155 mm gun on a late-model M4 medium chassis. The M40 made a notable action debut

in a long-range bombardment of Cologne in early 1945. After the war M40s were supplied to many other nations including Britain, West Germany and Japan.

The design of the basic Sherman tank was itself kept as up-to-date as production recources and combat requirements would allow. The Sherman was inherently simple in concept, designed for mass-production and for easy field maintenance by men with limited training. As such it was a considerable success, even though it fell short in many fighting qualities when compared to Germany's late-model PzKpfw IV and the Tigers and Panthers. It was relatively thinly armoured and by 1944 its 75 mm gun was long in the tooth and of no great value for knocking out Tiger and Panther tanks. Extra armour plates were added to protect the most vulnerable parts of the Sherman and, in 1943–1944, numerous production modifications were made. These included 'wet stowage' for the ammunition (ammunition fires were a frequent result of a hit prior to this), wider tracks, and a new suspension system called HVSS (horizontal volute suspension) which gave a smoother ride and was just as serviceable as the old vertical suspension. Hull modifications improved the shape and access,

Left: unloading Afrika Korps tanks at Tripoli in the summer of 1941. The 20 ton PzKpfw III shown was at this time the main tank of the panzer divisions. Model shown, the 'N', had a 7·5 cm low velocity gun (earlier versions had successively 3·7 cm, short 5 cm and long 5 cm guns).

Below: the Universal Carrier was developed in 1940 from the various small carriers previously used by the British. Many special purpose variants were developed, such as the Wasp flame-thrower shown here. The flame fuel was carried in the rear mounted tank with the flame projector in the super-structure front. This type remained in service for several years – this one was actually photographed in 1955.

Left: Calliope was the name given to this rocket-firing version of the M4 series Sherman tank, which gave devastating support fire. The simple frame held 60 4·6 in rocket tubes and a stay attached to the gun was used to elevate the array to the requisite firing angle. Note the camouflage foliage and also the 'grousers' (extensions) on the track shoes which gave added grip in snow or mud.

Below: the lack of a heavy tank in the US Army in 1944 was partly overcome by adding an extra layer of armour plate to some 254 standard M4A3 vehicles. New heavy (150 mm) turret armour and 100 mm hull armour were main changes. Vehicle shown has 76 mm gun, but most had the 75 mm weapon. Designation was M4A3E2 heavy assault tank, but it was popularly called 'Jumbo'. An unmodified M4 Sherman is seen in background.

Opposite, top: Cromwell IV (passing a destroyed German Panther) was the best British tank of 1944. It had a 75 mm gun, weighed 27 tons, and a 40 mph top speed. It was a direct development from earlier British cruiser tanks.

Opposite, below: the Churchill Crocodile was a successful flame-thrower design used in 1944–45. The fuel trailer was armoured and could be jettisoned when empty, after which the tank operated in the normal way. This was one of the 'funnies' developed for the invasion of Europe.

and eventually a new enlarged turret with a high velocity 76 mm gun was added to boost the vehicle's firepower. Gradually the various Sherman models (mostly with different engines) were rationalised and by 1944 production was concentrated on three models, the original Wright-engined M4, the M4A2, with GM diesel engine (mainly used for supply to Allied forces) and the M4A3 with Ford GAA gasoline engine, the favoured model for US Army service. All had the late modifications described.

Concentration on medium and light tanks meant that output could be enormous and production swift. The U.S. Army was hardly interested in heavy tanks until late in the war when events brought it into the race for bigger and better firepower. A heavy tank had been designed in 1940, envisaged as a companion model for the M3 medium tank. This heavy tank, the M6, was built in several experimental forms with varying combinations of armament and construction. However, trials showed a few shortcomings, and at 45 tons it was considered too heavy

and too prominent a target. Also it took up the shipping space of two or three Shermans, so no big production order for the M6 was placed. In 1942 came the T14, in effect an enlarged version of the Sherman intended for Anglo-American service. However, the British lost interest in 1943 as it was not adequately armed.

Once the Sherman was in production the US Ordnance Department started work on its planned successor and built a number of interesting prototypes in the T20 series of medium tanks. One model had an automatic turret and another, the T23, saw limited production but no combat service. The U.S. Army were happy with the Sherman so little progress was made towards its successor. With the opening of the second front in Europe in June 1944, the American armoured divisions therefore lacked a heavy tank. To make up for this some Shermans were given much additional armour, and wide tracks to act as what amounted to 'substitute' heavy tanks. The design, the M4A3E2, 'Jumbo' proved quite successful.

Meanwhile the Sherman itself was up-gunned successfully with the bigger turret and 76 mm gun from the T23 tank, and still the army was happy. However the Ordnance Department carried on with their development work and by late 1944 had produced an enlarged version of the T23, the T26 medium tank, which weighed over 45 tons and had a 90 mm gun.

The army divisions in France showed little interest in this until the 'Battle of the Bulge', the Ardennes Offensive of December 1944, when the Germans drove a massive wedge into the American front. The German offensive was spearheaded by Tigers, Panthers, and King Tigers, in a massive concentration of tank power assembled in a last attempt to push the Allies back, or at least divide their front.

The inadequacy of the Sherman against the big German tanks suddenly changed the army's attitude and the call went out for the T26 to be built and sent to France. Production had already been organised for T26 and as the M26 Pershing (by then re-classed as a heavy tank) the vehicle was rushed to France. Early vehicles arrived in February 1945, too late for the 'Battle of the Bulge', but in time to be blooded in action before the war ended.

The British also lagged in the race for better firepower and Vickers made a version of the American 75 mm gun which was fitted to late marks of Churchill (Mks. VI and VII, 1944) and the Cromwell IV tank, latest in the cruiser tank line. In each case this was just about the largest gun which could be fitted within the physical restrictions of the turret ring. (This restriction in turn was due mainly to width limitations imposed in pre-war days so that all tanks could be transported on rail flat cars).

When the Tiger tank first appeared late in 1942 it was already realised by the British that larger anti-tank guns were required. An effort to produce a so-called '3-inch Gun Carrier' based on the Churchill chassis showed some promise in 1941. This project utilised redundant 3 inch AA guns. A small production run was completed but the vehicle was never used in combat and the project foundered in indecision—the question of whether the vehicle should be a tank corps or artillery responsibility bogged down progress

for months. The 17 pdr appeared as a new anti-tank gun design in 1942 – it first entered service on a field mount in Tunisia in early 1943 – and a project was put forward to mount it in the Cromwell. Due to this vehicle's restricted width and the gun's weight, it was necessary to re-design the basic Cromwell to take the gun. It turned out longer and wider, with a new turret; and it was re-named the Challenger.

A proportion of Challengers were put into all armoured divisions to take on the bigger German tanks, but then there were numerous delays in the programme, and major problems with the turret and traverse gear. So although the Challenger was needed for the Normandy invasion in June

1944 and 200 had been completed, the tank was not battle-worthy in time. In particular it lacked adequate provision for water-proofing, a critical factor for amphibious operations. Fortunately the Sherman tank had been examined in November 1943 for possible conversion to carry a 17 pdr, as a safeguard against shortcomings in the Challenger. By turning the gun on its side and adding a counterweight to the turret the modification was just possible. The new vehicle was called the Sherman Firefly and it completely eclipsed the Challenger (only a few of which were used), becoming Britain's most powerfully armed gun-tank to see combat in the Second World War. It proved a good match for the Panther and Tiger

and its only major shortcoming was its scarcity – the few vehicles available in June 1944 were rationed out sparsely among the armoured divisions.

The British attempted to make other vehicles with the 17 pdr. The Comet was a redesigned Cromwell with a reduced length 17 pdr (the so-called 77 mm gun) which entered service early in 1945. It served for years after the war, as the last of the run of cruiser tanks based on the original Christie idea modified by the British. The Black Prince was an enlarged version of the Churchill, also to take the 17 pdr gun. It was even slower than the Churchill (8 mph) however, and by the time it appeared the war had ended and there was no production order.

The Comet (right) was a greatly improved successor to the Cromwell, which first entered service at the end of 1944. Weight was 32½ tons, length 21½ ft (gun excluded), and it had 100 mm armour. Its engine was the Rolls-Royce Meteor a 600 bhp derated version of the famous Merlin aero engine first used in the Cromwell.
Below: Black Prince looked like the Churchill but was bigger all round and carried the 17 pdr gun. Vauxhall Motors designed this model but only six prototypes were built, in 1945. Weight was 50 tons, length 29 ft, maximum armour thickness 152 mm.

Above: contrast in sizes of the two principal German tank destroyers of the 1944–45 period. The little Jagdpanzer 38(t) Hetzer 7·5 cm Pak 39 was a self-propelled gun conversion of the Czech-built PzKpfw 38(t) tank shown on page 52. The Hetzer weighed 15¾ tons and was 16 ft long (over hull, 20½ ft over gun). It had 60 mm armour (maximum), a top speed of 25 mph and a crew of four. A flame-thrower version was also built. Over 1,500 Hetzers were built, and after 1945 some were used by the Swiss Army.

The Jagdpanther (right) was based on the Panther chassis and had a limited traverse 8·8 cm Pak 43. It weighed 45 tons, had 80 mm armour, and was 32 ft 4 in long over the gun. About 230 were built. This photograph shows the typical German colour schemes of the later war period, 'sand' being the basic factory finish. The other colours were applied over the basic sand by the vehicle crew, using a water soluble paste, which was issued in a range of colours.
Left: crew of a PzKpfw III relaxing in front of their vehicle. Black uniform was usually worn by German tank crews.

The Sherman DD (Duplex Drive) was a major type of special purpose vehicle. The adaptation allowed the tank to 'swim' ashore from a landing craft. The canvas screens were raised by air tubes and struts; propulsion was by propellors driven by a power take-off. With canvas lowered (above) the tank fought in its normal role.

British tank development in the Second World War culminated with the Centurion, a design which embodied all the lessons of previous efforts and for which the old dimensional restrictions were lifted so that allowance could be made in hull and chassis for future development. The old division into 'infantry' and 'cruiser' tank was ignored and the Centurion was the first of the type which were later simply known as 'battle tanks'. Horstmann spring suspension was used (the Christie type now being too

flimsy) and the 40 ton vehicle had a 52 mm frontal armour and the 17 pdr as main armament. A well-sloped hull front, boat-shaped hull, wide tracks and a roomy turret were main features. Six prototypes were built under the design parentage of Leyland Motors, all with varying secondary armament and some mechanical variations for test. By the time the Centurion prototypes had been rushed to units in Germany however, the war had ended, so these machines were never tested in battle against their intended adversaries,

the Panther and King Tiger.

On the Eastern Front, at the same time, the Russians had produced a fine new design of their own the IS-3, a new version of the Josef Stalin tank. This had the same armament as earlier Stalins, the 122 mm gun, but the whole vehicle was now given a new low silhouette with an 'inverted frying pan' turret and a streamlined slope-sided hull of excellent shape for the elimination of shot traps and deflection of shells. As with the T-34 before it, the IS-3 was a fundamental step forward in

Left: Matilda Baron was an early type of mine-clearing tank developed in Britain. Bedford truck engines drove the rotor arms. This type entered service in 1943 but was not used in action, being superseded by the Sherman Crab.
Below: the Churchill AVRE was another important special purpose type. It had a demolition gun for assault work. It was used for a number of functions, manned by Royal Engineers, as a fascine carrier and bridge-layer with light box girder assault bridge. Fittings to take these (shown on the vehicles here) were built into the AVRE, which was a conversion of the standard Churchill tank.

the evolution of tank design, and its influence is seen in most other tanks produced since then. The IS-3 was too late for war service but it was the most powerful tank in the world in 1945 and gave the Soviet Army a distinct lead in tank technology for some years after the war.

The major contribution to tank development made by the British during the war years was in the field of special purpose vehicles – tanks adapted to perform specific battlefield roles. British ingenuity was seen in a whole

succession of weird designs intended to facilitate the advance of armoured divisions in the amphibious invasion of the Continent and the subsequent fighting advance into Germany. The armies of other nations never really got involved in special purpose vehicles to any large extent (although tank recovery vehicles were of course used, as were tanks adapted to carry bridges).

Like all other military developments there was a cause. And the cause in this case was the need to breach the notorious 'West Wall', the formidable

beach defence system built along the Channel coast of France by the Germans in 1940–42. An analysis of the Dieppe raid in 1942 showed a need for assault vehicles to destroy enemy strongpoints at short range, carpet layers to make trackways off the beaches, bridging vehicles to assist following tanks over a sea wall and subsequently over inland obstructions, deep wading recovery tanks to 'rescue' swamped tanks on the beaches, tanks with charge placing equipment to blow up major obstacles, and mine clearing tanks to 'sweep' mine-free paths.

A special unit, 79th Armoured Division, was formed under a veteran Tank Corps officer, General P. Hobart, to develop and man the new equipment. Literally scores of designs were produced, some were no more than experimental but many which were adopted and standardised. A selection of the most important types are illustrated and some of the classes of vehicle are summarised below:

DD or Duplex-Drive: 'Swimming' tanks with propeller drive via a power take-off from the main drive. Collapsible canvas screens gave bouyancy and these tanks left their landing craft ahead of the main force and 'swam' ashore to land ahead of the first infantry. Valentines and Shermans were converted to DD tanks.

Flails or Crabs: Tank with a chain beating device carried ahead of the vehicle on framework and driven from the main engine. The chains were on a rotor and beat the ground ahead of the vehicle to explode any mines in its path. Following tanks kept to the

'swept' lane. Shermans were converted to Crabs. This type of vehicle was earlier originated at Alamein when big mine-fields were first encountered. In the desert Matilda (Barons) and Valentines (Scorpions) were similar but less refined vehicles to the Crab.

AVRE (Assault Vehicle Royal Engineers): Converted Churchill tank with demolition mortar, the 'Flying Dustbin' – literally a bomb which destroyed concrete pillboxes. The vehicle

Above: the LVT(A) 3 with 75 mm howitzer in an open topped turret was a development of the original Alligator LVT – armed versions of the LVT (another had a 37 mm gun) were invaluable in giving support fire in amphibious operations in the Pacific islands by US forces. Below: the ubiquitous M3A1 half track was the most numerous of a whole series of externally similar vehicles developed for the US Army from 1938 onwards. Simpler than the German half-tracks, the American vehicles had the same function. Although phased out by the US Army in 1945, many other armies still used these American built half-tracks well into the 1970s, the Israeli Defence Forces being a major user.

Above: the diminutive M9 Locust light tank was originally designed to be carried slung under the belly of a transport plane. It was eventually carried in the airborne role in the Hamilcar glider, a purpose built tank carrier which it is seen leaving.
Below: the LVT(A) 4, Buffalo, was a development from the Alligator. It was armoured and had a rear ramp to the cargo compartment. Hull shape was the same as the LVTs shown on the opposite page.

also carried demolition equipment, fascines or cribs to be dropped into ditches, and later an optional dozer blade. It could also carry and drop from sheerlegs a light SBG bridge.
Bridgelayer: Britain developed several vehicles of this type, the Churchill Tank Bridge being the most important in 1944. It could span a 30 ft gap and support a 40 ton load. The bridge was carried on a turretless Churchill and launched hydraulically.
Crocodile: This was a flamethrowing

tank, basically a Churchill towing a trailer with fuel to supply a projector which replaced the hull machine gun. The Americans developed several flamethrowers of their own for fitting to the Sherman tanks and these were mainly used in the fighting against tenacious Japanese forces on the Pacific islands. Flamethrower versions of the Universal Carrier were also developed by the British, and these were known as Ronsons and Wasps.

Two other types of vehicle which became practical propositions in the Second World War were the tracked infantry carrier and the airborne tank.

The armoured infantry carrier, in half-track form, originated before the war in Germany and America and was developed during the war. Full tracked carriers able to carry whole sections of infantry originated in 1944 when the Canadian First Army made some 'Kangaroos' by removing turrets from existing tanks (Canadian-built Rams) and used them as troop carriers. Some Priests with the guns removed similarly adapted and armoured infantry became an important spearhead of the Allied advances in 1945.

Airborne tanks had been thought of before the war by Christie in America and by the Russians. They were not developed however, and the British Tetrarch, last of the light tanks, was used in an airborne role, carried in the specially designed Hamilcar glider. Some vehicles were air-landed in Normandy in June 1944, where they had more novelty value than tactical worth. The American M9 Locust light tank, designed to be air-lifted under the belly of a C-54 cargo plane, was also used in small numbers, carried by gliders, at the Rhine crossing early in 1945.

Both these developments were really forerunners of things to come and tracked carriers and air-portable AFVs really came into their own in the years after the war.

Amphibious vehicles were another successful special purpose development in the Second World War. Britain had experimented with some floating vehicles, the Tank Mk. IX, modified and Medium Mk. D modified back in 1919, then in the 1920s and 1930s Vickers produced some amphibious light tanks with bouyancy

The IS-3 'Josef Stalin' was the most powerfully armed tank in the world when it appeared in the Allied Victory Parade in Berlin 1945. Combating the threat of the IS-3 kept other tank designers busy in the 'Cold War' years of the 1950s and 1960s. The Stalin's features of a low 'inverted frying pan' turret, low silhouette, and big gun influenced all subsequent battle tank design. The American M47 of the 1950s (seen, bottom, in French service) was a development from the 1944 M26 Pershing design, with a 90 mm gun; on paper it was no match for the Stalin.

tanks built into the structure and propellor drive via a power take-off from the engine. The British did not take these up, but they did interest other nations and the Soviet T-37 was one result.

For assault landing operations the Japanese developed several amphibious tanks. The most ingenious and most effective was the Type 2 which was a development from the Kyu-Go Type 95 light tank. Chassis, engine, suspension and mechanical features were as for the Type 95 but there was a new large capacity hull and flotation chambers. There were two propellor shafts, rudders and a bilge pump as standard fittings. The flotation chambers (or

pontoons) were a distinctive feature; they gave the tank bouyancy when swimming towards the beach and were released by easing off two handwheels once ashore.

The Americans developed a unique type, the Alligator, a cargo carrier initially designed for work in the Everglades Swamps. This interested the U.S. Marines who ordered duplicates in 1941. For the 'island hopping' campaigns in the Pacific in 1942–45 these vehicles, LVTs (landing vehicles, tracked) were ideal and saw wide service. Later came an armoured version the LVT(A). Another version the LVT(A)-4 had a rear ramp which allowed it to carry a Jeep and light guns. This type was also used by the British and figured prominently in the Rhine crossing of early 1945. To the British it was known as the Water Buffalo, later just Buffalo.

The Americans produced an armed version of the Alligator with a 37 mm gun and the turret of the M3 light tank, the LVT(A)-2. Another version was the LVT(A)-3 with 75 mm howitzer in a turret from the M8 howitzer motor carriage. These two vehicles were virtually amphibious tanks, though not classed as such by the Americans. Water propulsion was achieved by the tracks, each shoe having scoop shaped 'grousers' to push the water. Direction was achieved by jets of water.

MODERN ARMOUR

For at least a decade after the end of the Second World War most of the world's major armies used wartime equipment or designs originated during the war, as was the case in the 1920s.

The US Army in particular had embarked on a major rationalisation programme in 1944–45, in an attempt to cut down on the fast proliferating numbers of vehicle types. The plan was to produce standardised chassis in the light, medium and heavy classes and build a tank and special purpose vehicles on the common chassis within each class.

The 'Light Weight Combat Team' was based on a new light tank design, the M24 Chaffee, which entered service in 1944. This 17½ ton vehicle had a 75 mm gun with a concentric recoil device which enabled it to be installed in a compact mount. The 'Light Weight' team included an AA tank, a mortar carrier, a howitzer carriage, and a recovery vehicle, although the latter was not put into production.

The 'Medium Weight Combat Team' was based on the M4A3 Sherman and included the M7B1 Priest and M32 Recovery Vehicle. The 'Heavy Weight Combat Team' was based on the M26 Pershing, again with gun carriage and recovery vehicle variants. Half-tracks and armoured cars were soon dropped from US armoured divisions and a 'full-track' policy was instituted.

The British peacetime army had the Centurion Mk III as its first quantity production vehicle. This had a 20 pdr gun. The other British vehicles still in wide service were the Comet, Cromwell, and Churchill. The Cromwell was given a new lease of life in 1950

Top: the M24 Chaffee was a fine light tank design from America, greatly superior to the earlier light tank designs for the reconnaissance role. Most nations within the American sphere of influence used Chaffees in the 1945–70 period (this one belongs to the Japanese Defence Forces). Main weapon was a 75 mm gun.

Above: An early model of the Soviet T54, successor to the T-34. This one is travelling with its turret traversed aft. In the medium class, its 100 mm gun outclassed many heavier and more sophisticated tanks used by other nations. Vehicle weighed 36 tons and was 21 ft long. Maximum armour thickness was about 85 mm.

Armoured cars, like the Ferret (above), proved ideal vehicles for 'brush fire' wars of the 1960s, being air-portable and cheaper to operate than tanks. The Ferret is pictured in Malaya in 1960. It is a Mk.I (originally without a turret) modified to Mk.2 standard. Opposite, top: Germany's Leopard 'standardpanzer' was a contemporary of the Chieftain and AMX 30 as a main battle tank for the 1970s.

Right: the M113 was an American armoured personnel carrier of the 1960s, widely used by NATO armies (this one is in Federal German service). It made extensive use of aluminium armour for lightness.

when it was fitted with a new large turret and 20 pdr gun (in this guise it was known as the Charioteer).

The Soviets had the IS-3, the most advanced tank in the World in 1945. The T-34 was gradually replaced from about 1950 with the much improved T-54, a lower vehicle with a 100 mm gun, but the T-34 remained in wide service into the 1970s, especially with the armies of Soviet satellite states.

Two unusual vehicles of the 1946–47 period were the British A39 Tortoise and the American T95/T28. These both owed their appearance to the big German tanks of 1944 and were designed to be able to outshoot the Jagdtiger. The 78 ton Tortoise had 225 mm armour and mounted a massive 32 pdr gun. Its design was initiated in 1944 but by the time the six prototypes were built the war was long over and the huge vehicle was unwanted. A similar fate awaited the T95/T28, which was an even bigger vehicle (90–95 tons) with novel features which included twin tracks, the outer pair removable to reduce overall width and weight. This immense vehicle had a 105 mm gun and it too was declared obsolete almost as soon as it was completed.

In fact, the heavy tank policy largely dropped by America and Britain during the war, enjoyed a major revival which lasted for several years. The cause was the formidable Soviet IS-3 tank and the need was for tanks which could outshoot it in battle. The British revived a wartime concept for a 'universal' chassis which could be used as the basis for a cruiser type or an infantry type tank. This was evolved into the Centurion which in 1945 became the only British battle tank. However, the 17 pdr and later 20 pdr guns of the Centurion were considered inadequate to counter the longer range of the Stalin's 122 mm gun, so the 'universal' chassis design was adapted to make a so-called 'heavy gun tank', the Conqueror. The sole function of this tank was to strengthen and pro-

tect the Centurion tank squadrons. The 120 mm gun was adapted from an American design, with automatic loading. The 65 ton Conqueror was in service from 1955–66 when the introduction of a powerful 105 mm gun for the Centurion rendered the Conqueror unnecessary.

The American equivalent of the Conqueror was the M103 120 mm Gun Combat Tank which saw service with US forces in Europe from 1953 until 1965. It had the same gun as the Conqueror, weighed $62\frac{1}{2}$ (US) tons, had a speed of 21 mph, but a range of only 80 miles. It had many operating faults and was not universally liked. When the Americans adopted the

British 105 mm gun for their main battle tanks, the M103, like the Conqueror, was speedily retired. Both were anachronisms which suffered tactical limitations of the sort which dogged the German Jagdtigers and King Tigers of 1944–45.

The Korean War of 1950–53 provided the first opportunity since 1945 for AFVs to prove themselves in action. Generally speaking the terrain was not suitable for large scale tank actions, but the outstanding success in small battles was the British Centurion (in its Mk III form) which was more than a match for the T-34/85s of the Koreans and Chinese. The war gave great impetus to rearmament

Top: the big Conqueror tank with its side skirts removed to show the suspension bogies. Note the very wide tracks, and fume extractor sleeve on the 120 mm gun (turret is traversed aft).
Right: the M19 AA gun motor carriage was built on the Chaffee chassis as part of the Light Weight Combat Team. Twin 40 mm Bofors guns were fitted.

programmes in Britain and America, with new generations of vehicles replacing the wartime designs.

In America in the early 1950s the M41 Walker Bulldog replaced the M24 Chaffee in the light tank class, and the M48 Medium Tank (Patton) replaced the M26 Pershing (and its modernised derivatives the M46 and M47). A new type of full-track armoured personnel carrier, the M59, was developed to carry infantry within the armoured formations. This was a fully enclosed vehicle with a rear door and represented a considerable advance over earlier APCs, like M3 half-tracks and other open-topped vehicles. The M48 Medium Tank family included numerous special purpose vehicles – mine-clearers, bridge-layers, and dozers for example. As the M48 had been rushed into production for the Korean conflict it suffered numerous design defects which were revealed in service, and led to substantial changes in later models. A diesel engine, better fire control, a new cupola, extra fuel storage, suspension modifications and so on greatly improved the breed.

The M48 had only a 90 mm gun, like its progenitor the Pershing, and this was inferior to both the 120 mm gun of the Stalin and the 100 mm gun of the T-54. The new British-developed L7 105 mm L/51 gun was tested on a M48, proved successful and was ordered for production. In 1960 the modified design with the 105 mm gun was designated M60 and rapidly replaced the M48. A further development with M60 was the M60A1E2 which had the Shillelegh, a 152 mm howitzer able to fire either conventional shells or an anti-tank missile, radio-guided and fin stabilised. This weapon was the subject of considerable development problems. It was also the main armament of a new light tank, the XM551 Sheridan which entered service in 1970. M48/M60 'family' vehicles included the M88 recovery vehicle, M48, or M60 AVLB bridge-layer, and TII8EI

Left: a Conqueror tank displays its immense size, almost 13 ft wide and 11½ ft high. Armour thickness was about 200 mm. The 120 mm gun was used on its American equivalent, the M103.
Below: Anglo-American exercises in Germany in 1970 – British infantry with a US Army M60A1 main battle tank. This vehicle had the British 105 mm gun and is the most recent in the line of development reaching back to the M26, of 1945. Note the infra-red searchlight.

Armour in the 1960s. Above: French paratroops leap from the back of a British Centurion Mk.8 main battle tank during an exercise in Germany. In various forms, this 50 ton vehicle served the British Army from 1945 until the early 1970s, and is in service with many other armies.

Right: the Federal German Army continued the wartime type of tank destroyer vehicle in their modern 90 mm Kanonenjagdpanzer. This low 23 ton vehicle had a limited traverse mount with the same gun as the American M47 and M48 battle tanks. It is 20 ft long and has a top speed of 49 mph. It is only 6½ ft high.

Opposite, top: the Ferret Mk.2 armoured car saw wide service with the British Army from 1955 well into the 1970s, mainly in reconnaissance roles. It weighs just under 4½ tons, has 12 mm armour, and a speed of 45 mph.

Opposite, bottom: the Saladin armoured car, a six-wheeler with a 76 mm gun, weighed over 10½ tons. Saladins and Ferrets were sold to many other nations in the 1960s, and were made by the famous firm of Alvis.

armoured engineer vehicle. All had the M48/M60 chassis.

In Britain there was a slightly different pattern of development. The Centurion proved to be a sound design capable of enormous development. The Korean War proved the vehicle's quality and its stabilisation and control system, later based on the use of a ranging machine gun which fired tracer as an aiming guide, proved far more effective than the sophisticated optical and computerised control systems used by the Americans. With the British-developed 105 mm L/51 gun the later Centurions kept well up to date. There was also a family of special purpose Centurion vehicles, including bridgelayer, AVRE and recovery vehicles.

In the early 1960s all the major European nations developed new main battle tanks. France produced the AMX 30, Germany the Leopard, and Britain the Chieftain. The first two had the British L7 105 mm gun while the Chieftain had a new 120 mm gun. This was designed to outrange all potential enemy tanks and in the Chieftain firepower, armour and speed were considered in that order of priority. The ammunition storage limitations of a big gun (a particular drawback in the Russian Stalin tanks) were largely overcome by using a bagged rather than a cased cartridge. A new multi-fuel engine, the Leyland L.60, was used and a low overall height was achieved, mainly by placing the driver in a semi-reclining rather than a seated position.

The French and German designs started life to a common requirement, for a 'European' tank with the possibility of standardising it for the West European forces of the late 1960s. The

Top to bottom: Centurion Bridgelayer emplaced and recovered its bridge by means of hydraulically operated arm. Bridge supports the weight of main battle tanks; bridgelayers are used in all combat tank regiments. The French AMX 30 displays the 'inverted frying pan' turret and the low hull common to all major main battle tanks in the 1970s. The notable French light tank of the 1960s was the AMX 13, with oscillating turret which allowed a big 75 mm gun to be carried on a relatively small (14 ton 14 ft long) vehicle. The Soviet ASU 85 was a tank destroyer on a relatively light chassis which was air-transportable.

order of priority was considered to be speed, firepower and armour. Speed was, of course, dependent on armour, and the Franco-German military staffs considered that excessive armour thickness had lost its importance in the missile age. Hence the Leopard and AMX 30 were fast, with a top speed of around 40 mph compared with the Chieftain's 25 mph. They had a lighter, less powerful gun, the British L7 105 mm weapon, and their weight was less, at around 44 tons compared to the Chieftain's weight of about 58 tons. The French side of the 'European' tank programme eventually split from the Germans and the AMX 30 finally emerged as a different design from the Leopard, although both had similar characteristics. The Leopard proved the most commercially successful of the three designs with vehicles, being supplied to Belgium, the Netherlands, Norway, and Italy, and thus coming quite close to the original idea of a single battle tank for West Europe. Recovery and bridgelaying variants of all three types were produced.

The most original of all post-war battle tank designs however, emanated in Sweden. Here the famous Bofors firm produced the turretless S-tank, with a fixed 105 mm gun and a sophisticated hydro-pneumatic steering system, linked to the gun sight. The entire tank was used for instantly aiming the gun by swinging it to the correct bearing for engaging a target. Both the commander and driver-cum-gunner had cupolas, sights and duplicate gun controls. The gun was automatically loaded and the suspension was locked automatically as the gun fired, in order to give momentary stability. Another innovation in this design was the use of a Rolls-Royce diesel motor for cruising and a small Boeing gas turbine for bursts of high speed running in combat. Lacking a conventional turret, the S-tank was very low and with a weight of about 37 tons was notably light. In fact it was the most progressive step forward in tank development since 1945, although some experts considered the lack of a turret to be

a disadvantage as fire to the flanks while on the move was precluded. Among its standard fittings were a built-in collapsible flotation screen – later adopted in some British vehicles – and a dozer blade.

From the many notable new AFV designs of the 1950s and 1960s it is possible to mention only a few. While the light tank had generally been dropped during the Second World War, the post-War French Army had a novel series of lightweight (rather than light) tanks in the AMX 13 series. The basic AMX 13 tank had its 75 mm gun in an oscillating turret. This was in two parts, split horizontally; the lower turret half held the gun trunnions so that the gun and turret were independent in movement from the tank, rather like a gimbal-mounted compass in a ship. The AMX 13 was an effective vehicle with big hitting power for its size. Variants included a bridgelayer anti-aircraft vehicle, self-propelled guns and troop carrier – in all a fine range of common chassis vehicles.

New self-propelled guns were produced by most major nations, main vehicles being the 90mm Jagdpanzer (West Germany), the ASU-85 (Russia) and the PVKV 71 (Sweden), all vehicles with limited traverse high velocity mounts which were similar in layout to Second World War tank hunters. Self-propelled field howitzers generally replaced the towed artillery of previous years within armoured

formations. Notable types included the Abbott 105 mm (Britain) and the M108 105 mm and M109 155 mm (USA). These were vehicles with the armament in enclosed turrets, roomy hulls, and a flotation capability.

Armoured cars had a new lease of life in the post-war period. Improvements in automotive technology meant that in cross-country performance wheeled AFVs were almost as good as tanks. Six- or eight-wheel drive was technically possible and some designers also came up with adjustable suspension systems.

One of the most effective armoured car designs was the British Saladin, a tough well-armoured six-wheeler with a 76 mm gun packing a punch as powerful as most British war-time tanks. The Saladin was similar in chassis layout to the M38 armoured car built by Chevrolet in 1945 for the US Army, but not adopted. With a hull like a tank, the Saladin could in fact, undertake all the reconnaissance and patrol work formerly carried out by light tanks, and look after itself admirably in a straight 'shooting match' as well. The Saladin saw wide service and was used by many foreign armies as well as the British for whom it was designed. The Saracen armoured personnel carrier and Stalwart amphibious load carrier were further well-known vehicles sharing the same adaptable six-wheel chassis.

A very fine French design of the 1950s was the Panhard EBR75, an

Latest Russian tank in 1970 was the T-62, a development from the T-54 series. Infra-red sights, night driving lights, and all-round vision cupolas are modern tank fittings.

Modern battlefield weapons include a wide variety of missiles and rockets which offer an additional threat to enemy fighting vehicles. The Swingfire (top) is a British anti-tank missile, wire-guided and optically sighted. It is being fired from an FV 438 carrier vehicle. The Honest John (below) is a first generation tactical artillery missile, virtually a modern replacement for corps or divisional artillery with a 12 mile range, at one time used by most NATO armies.

Opposite: the Scorpion is a British lightweight combat reconnaissance vehicle (not strictly classed as a tank) designed to be air-portable and part of a family of complementary battlefield vehicles on a common chassis. Extensive use is made of aluminium alloys in its construction, and it is powered by the famous Jaguar XK engine. The official designation of this version is CVR(T)FF Scorpion.

eight wheel drive vehicle with the four centre wheels in the form of steel discs which were used cross-country but raised clear for road running. Like the AMX 13 the vehicle had an oscillating turret with 75 mm gun. Top speed was over 60 mph. There were several different versions of this vehicle, including an armoured personnel carrier.

In Switzerland excellent armoured cars were built by Mowag on a simple but tough four wheel drive chassis. Tank destroyer, mortar carrier, personnel carrier and rocket carrier versions were built but the design was a latecomer (in 1959) and its potential overseas markets were already well filled by the Saladin and EBR designs.

America was the one nation which dropped armoured cars completely in 1945 and since then only a few American car designs have appeared. The main vehicle has been the Commando, which saw service in Vietnam, where the sort of guerilla warfare encountered makes the armoured car a useful item of equipment.

The trend since about 1955 in all the major armies of the world has been towards the lighter type of fighting vehicle which can be air-freighted quickly to the scene of action. The Soviet Union was very early in the field with the PT-76 reconnaissance tank, a 16-ton vehicle with built-in buoyancy for flotation, and water propulsion units. The BTR 50 personnel carrier and ASU-85 tank destroyer used the same light chassis and the design was also adapted as a carrier vehicle for the Frog tactical missile

and Gannef anti-aircraft missile. A very small vehicle was the ASU-57, a low open tank destroyer, with high velocity 57 mm gun. The Russians also built a series of wheeled troop carriers of which the BTR 152 was an early post-war example. Based on a Zil 6×6 truck chassis it had an armoured open body similar in style to earlier armoured half-tracks. A unique feature of this vehicle was a means of varying the tyre pressure to suit the surface, the driver controlling this at will. A more recent troop carrier widely used by the Russians was the BTR 60, a low eight-wheeler with excellent shape and performance.

The British Scorpion is essentially a lightweight tracked reconnaissance vehicle, making extensive use of aluminium-based armour plate and cap-

able of 50 mph – a speed achieved by using the famous Jaguar XK 4.2 litre engine. The Scorpion is intended as a Saladin replacement and a whole range of specialist vehicles on the same chassis has also been developed. These include Scimitar (reconnaissance) Spartan (troop carrier) Samaritan (ambulance), Sultan (command), Samson (recovery), and Striker (Swingfire anti-tank missile).

The modern armoured formation has to be prepared to fight in conditions of nuclear warfare so the armoured personnel carrier has become a fully enclosed vehicle, able to deliver infantrymen safely at their point of attack. Classic contemporary APCs are the M113, built in America and used by many armies, and the FV 432, a very similar British vehicle.

Tanks and armoured vehicles now face the threat not only of the anti-tank gun and rocket launcher but also

anti-tank missiles like the Malkara SS11, Swingfire, and Snapper, all small wire or beam guided weapons carried on tanks or other armoured vehicles. Current armoured vehicles have infra-red night vision sights and vision aids, air-conditioning (in many cases), computerised fire control equipment, multi-fuel engines (in some cases) and mechanical components such as engines and transmissions which can be quickly replaced as units to speed field repairs and maintenance.

With all major armies of the world equipped for fighting with or without nuclear weapons, for full-scale conflicts or low key guerilla wars, the next 60 years of AFV development should be as eventful and interesting as the last 60 years.

The American M107 gun motor carriage was one of a big family of different types built on a standard 25 ton chassis. Simplicity of maintenance — using the power pack principle — and a stable gun platform were requirements for the chassis. The suspension locks itself hydraulically when the gun is fired and a recoil spade at rear anchors the vehicle. Gun is 175 mm calibre with an 18 mile range, firing nuclear or conventional HE shells. The M107 and the similar M110 (203 mm howitzer) serve with several NATO armies.

PRINCIPAL TANKS

Type	Armour (mm) max/min	Weight (tons)	Length (overall) ft	in	Width (overall) ft	in	Height (overall) ft	in	Engine/bhp	Speed mph	Crew	Armament main/ secondary	Period of Service
Mark I Male (GB)	10/6	28	26	5	13	9½	8	2	Daimler 6 cyl/105	3.7	8	2× 6 pdr 4× MG	1916–17
Medium Mk A 'Whippet' (GB)	12/6	14	20	0	8	7	9	0	2× Tylor 4 cyl/90	8.3	3	3× MG	1917–22
A7V Sturmpanzerwagen (GER)	30/15	30	26	3	10	0½	10	10	2× Daimler 4 cyl/200	8	18	1× 57 mm 6× MG	1918
Christie T3 (M1931) (USA)	15/4	10.5	18	0	7	4	7	6	Liberty V-12/338	46.8 (wheels) 27.3 (tracks)	3	1× 37 mm 2× MG	1932–40
Renault FT (37 mm gun) (FR)	22/6	6.5	13	6	5	7½	7	0	Renault 4 cyl/35	4.8	2	1× 37 mm	1917–40
T-28 (USSR)	30/11	28.5	24	3	9	2½	9	3	M-17 V-12/500	23	6	1× 76.2 mm 2× MG	1933–41
Light Tank Mk VIA (GB)	14/4	5.2	12	11½	6	9	7	3½	Meadows/88	35	3	2× MG	1936–42
Char Somua S-35 (FR)	56/41	19.7	17	11	6	11	8	10	Somua V-8/190	23	3	1× 47 mm 1× MG	1938–40
Type 97 Chi-Ha (Japan)	25/10	14.3	18	0	7	7½	7	6	Mitsubishi V-12 diesel/170	23	4	1× 57 mm 2× MG	1937–45
PzKpfw IV Aus D (GER)	30/10	17 app	19	3	9	4	8	6	Maybach HL 120 TRM/320	25	5	1× 7.5 cm 2× MG	1940–42
Infantry Tank Mk II, Matilda II (GB)	78/13	26.5	18	5	8	6	8	0	2× AEC diesel/174	15	4	1× 2 pdr 1× MG	1939–42
Cruiser Tank Mk VI Crusader I (GB)	40/7	19	19	8	8	8	7	4	Nuffield Liberty/340	27	5	1× 2 pdr 2× MG	1941–43
Medium Tank T-34/76 (USSR)	45/14	26.3	20	0	9	9½	9	7	V-2-34 V-12/450	31	4	1× 76 mm 2× MG	1941–45
Heavy Tank KV-1 (USSR)	100/30	46.4	22	7	10	8½	8	9	V-2 V-12/550	22	5	1× 76 mm 3× MG	1940–45
PzKpfw IV Tiger 'E' (GER)	100/26	56	27	9	12	3	9	4¾	Maybach HL 210 P45/650	23	5	1× 8.8 cm 2× MG	1942–45
Light Tank (Stuart I) M3 (USA)	51/10	13.5	14	10¾	7	4	8	3	Continental W-670/250	36	4	1× 37 mm 1–3× MG	1941–45
Medium Tank (Sherman IV) M4A3 (USA)	75/12	34.25	20	7	8	9	9	0	Ford GAA/500	26	4	1× 75 mm 2–3× MG	1942–45
Gun Motor Carriage (Hellcat) M18 (USA)	12/7	20	21	10	9	9	8	5	Continental R-975/400	45	5	1× 76 mm 1× MG	1944–50
Heavy Tank (Pershing) M26 (USA)	102/13	46	28	10	11	6	9	1	Ford GAF V-8/500	20	5	1× 90 mm 3× MG	1944–52
Infantry Tank Mk IV Churchill VIII (GB)	152/25	40	25	2	10	8	8	0½	Bedford Twin-Six/350	16	5	1× 75 mm 2× MG	1944–54
Main Battle Tank Centurion 5 (GB)	152/17	56 app	32	3	11	1	9	7¾	Meteor 4B/650	21	4	1× 20 pdr 2× MG	1955–67
IS-3 Stalin Heavy Tank (USSR)	230/20	45.8	32	9	10	6	8	11	V-2-IS/519	23	4	1× 120 mm 2× MG	1945–
Main Battle Tank Leopard (W.GER)		42 app	31	4	10	8	7	10	Daimler Benz 838/840	41	4	1× 105 mm 2× MG	1966–
Main Battle Tank Chieftain 2 (GB)		55 app	32	4	12	0	8	3	L.60 Mk 4/730	25	4	1× 120 mm 2× MG	1969–
Main Battle Tank S-Tank (SWEDEN)		37	33	1¼	11	9½	6	9½	Rolls K.60 and Boeing 502; 240/490	31	3	1× 105 mm 3× MG	1968–